ONLY A TRILLION

ISAAC ASIMOV

ONLY
A TRILLION

ABELARD-SCHUMAN
LONDON AND NEW YORK

To

GERTRUDE

again

© Copyright 1957 by Isaac Asimov

Library of Congress Catalogue
Card Number 57-9947

Acknowledgment is made to Street & Smith Publications Inc., which published: *Hemoglobin and the Universe; Victory on Paper; The Abnormality of Being Normal; Planets Have an Air About Them; The Unblind Workings of Chance; The Trapping of the Sun; The Sea-Urchin and We; The Sound of Panting; The Marvellous Properties of Thiotimoline* and *Paté de Foie Gras*

London	New York	Toronto
Abelard Schuman	Abelard-Schuman	Abelard-Schuman
Limited	Limited	Canada Limited
8 King Street	6 West 57th Street	81 John Street

Printed in the United States of America

CONTENTS

INTRODUCTION

ONE of the stories my mother likes to tell about me as a child is that once, when I was nearly five, she found me standing rapt in thought at the curbing in front of the house in which we lived. She said, 'What are you doing, Isaac?' and I answered, 'Counting the cars as they pass.'

I have no personal memory of this incident but it must have happened, for I have been counting things ever since. At the age of nearly five I couldn't have known many numbers and, even allowing for the relatively few cars roaming the streets thirty years ago, I must have quickly reached my limit. Perhaps it was the sense of frustration I then experienced that has made me seek ever since for countable things that would demand higher and higher numbers.

With time I grew old enough to calculate the number of snow-flakes it would take to bury Greater New York under ten feet of snow and the number of raindrops it would take to fill the Pacific Ocean. There is even a chance that I was subconsciously driven to make chemistry my life-work out of a sense of gratitude to that science for having made it possible for me to penetrate beyond such things and take—at last—to counting atoms.

There is a fascination in large numbers which catches at most people, I think, even those who are easily made dizzy.

For instance, take the number one million; a 1 followed by six zeros; 1,000,000; or, as expressed by physical scientists, 10^6, which means 10 X 10 X 10 X 10 X 10 X 10.

Now consider what 'one million' means.

How much time must pass in order that a million seconds may elapse?—Answer: just over $11\frac{1}{2}$ days.

What about a million minutes?—Answer: just under 2 years.

How long a distance is a million inches?—Answer: just under 16 miles.

Assuming that every time you take a step your body moves forward about a foot and a half, how far have you gone when you take a million steps?—Answer: 284 miles.

In other words:

The secretary who goes off for a week to the mountains has less than a million seconds to enjoy herself.

The professor who takes a year's Sabbatical leave to write a book has just about half a million minutes to do it in.

Manhattan Island from end to end is less than a million inches long.

And, finally, you can walk from New York to Boston in less than a million steps.

Even so, you may not be impressed. After all, a jet plane can cover a million inches in less than a minute. At the height of World War II, the United States was spending a million dollars every six minutes.

So—— Let's consider a trillion. A trillion is a million million[1]; a 1 followed by 12 zeros; 1,000,000,000,000; 10^{12}.

A trillion seconds is equal to 31,700 years.

A trillion inches is equal to 15,800,000 miles.

In other words, a trillion seconds ago, Stone Age man lived in caves, and mastodons roamed Europe and North America.

Or, a trillion-inch journey will carry you 600 times around the Earth, and leave more than enough distance to carry you to the Moon and back.

And yet a good part of the chapters that follow ought to show you quite plainly that even a trillion can become a laughably small figure in the proper circumstances.

After considerable computation one day recently I said to my long-suffering wife: 'Do you know how rare astatine–215 is? If you inspected all of North and South America to a depth of ten miles, atom by atom, do you know how many atoms of astatine–215 you would find?'

My wife said, 'No. How many?'

To which I replied, 'Practically none. Only a trillion.'

---

[1] That is, according to American and French usage. In England, a billion is 10^{12} and a trillion is 10^{18}, that is, zeros are counted in groups of six, not in groups of three as in America and France. The American custom will be followed in this book, when a billion will mean 10^9 and a trillion 10^{12}.

CHAPTER ONE

THE ATOMS THAT VANISH

I THINK I can assume that the readers of this book all know that there are atoms which are unstable and which break down by ejecting particles from within their nuclei. Sometimes the ejection of one particle is sufficient to allow what remains of the nucleus to be stable. Sometimes a dozen or more particles must be ejected one after the other in order for stability to be attained.

In either case, the original atom is completely changed.

If you were to focus your attention on a particular one of these unstable atoms, it would be impossible for you or for anyone to tell when it would explode and eject a particle. It might do so the very next instant; it might stay put for a million years before doing so.

Dealing with a large group of objects, however, is not the same as dealing with only one object. Once you have a large group, you can use statistics to predict the future. The larger the group, the more accurate (percentage-wise) the predictions.

Given enough atoms, statistics will predict, for instance, that after a certain particular length of time, half of a quantity of a certain unstable atom will be broken down. After the same length of time, half of what is left will be broken down. After the same length of time, half of what is *still* left will be broken down, and so on as long as any of the atoms are left at all.

Each kind of unstable atom has its own characteristic time for half-breaking-down. This time is called the 'half-life'.

Let's see what this involves in a particular case. Suppose we take a kind of atom we will call Atom X and suppose that it has a half-life of exactly one day; twenty-four hours on the nose. Let's suppose, further, that at noon on January 1, 1957, you have in your possession 1,048,576 atoms of Atom X. What will happen if statistical laws are followed exactly?

The simplest way of answering that question is to present a table. For that reason, you are invited to look at Table I.

TABLE I

Date (*12 m.*)	No. of Atoms of Atom X left
January 1	1,048,576
January 2	524,288
January 3	262,144
January 4	131,072
January 5	65,536
January 6	32,768
January 7	16,384
January 8	8,192
January 9	4,096
January 10	2,048
January 11	1,024
January 12	512
January 13	256
January 14	128
January 15	64
January 16	32
January 17	16
January 18	8
January 19	4
January 20	2
January 21	1

Suppose that matters work out ideally and that we are down to a single atom by January 21. What happens to that atom? Statistics can't say exactly, but it can predict probabilities. For instance, the odds are even money that a single atom of Atom X will last one day or less and be gone by noon on January 22. The odds are 2 to 1 that it will be gone by noon on January 23; 4 to 1 that it will be gone by noon on January 24; and over a million to 1 that it will be gone by noon on February 11.

It's pretty safe to say, then, that of the more than a million atoms you started with at New Year's Day all would probably be gone within a month and almost certainly within six weeks.

A very important thing to remember, incidentally, is that it doesn't matter whether those million atoms of Atom X were heaped together in a pile to begin with, or scattered singly over the entire Earth. The end result is exactly the same either way.

But what if we were to begin with more than 1,048,576

atoms. Take an extreme case as an example. There are about 10^{50} atoms in the entire planet, Earth. (The number, 10^{50}, is a shorthand way of writing a number which consists of a 1 followed by 50 zeros. In other words, 10^{50} is a hundred trillion trillion trillion trillion). We are going to suppose now that the entire Earth is composed of Atom X exclusively. How long would they last?

The answer is about $5\frac{1}{2}$ months.

Of course, we don't have to stop with the Earth. It has been estimated that the number of atoms in the entire known Universe (including the Sun, the Moon, the planets, the stars and galaxies, the interstellar dust and gas) is about 10^{75}. If every atom in the entire Universe were Atom X, the whole supply would be gone in about $8\frac{1}{2}$ months.

So you see it is now possible to make a very comprehensive statement. When the Universe first came into being, a certain number of atoms of Atom X might have existed. If so, then *no matter how many of them existed*, not one of those original atoms of Atom X is left today.

But certain radioactive (*i.e.* unstable) atoms *do* exist today. If you have heard of no other examples, you have surely heard of uranium. The question, then, is under what conditions can radioactive atoms, formed at the time the Universe came into being, still exist today.

One way in which the existence of radioactive atoms can be stretched out is to have the individual atoms break down less frequently; that is, have longer half-lives.

To give you an idea of what the effect of half-life on atomic existence is, consider Table II. Such a table points out the fact that if the half-life is only long enough then the atoms will last as long as is desired.

Through several lines of evidence, astrophysicists have come to believe that some four or five billion years ago some kind of cosmic explosion took place, in the course of which the atoms, as we know them today, were formed. To have a round number, then, let us say that the Universe is five billion years old.

In a five-billion-year-old Universe, even atoms with half-lives of a thousand years (the longest considered in Table II)

TABLE II

If the half-life of an atom is ...	Then a Universe-full of such atoms will last ...
1 second	4 minutes
1 minute	4 hours
1 hour	10 days
1 day	8 months
1 week	5 years
1 month	20 years
1 year	250 years
1 decade	2,500 years
1 century	25,000 years
1 millennium	250,000 years

couldn't possibly have lasted to the present moment no matter how many had originally been formed. In fact, if we were to continue Table II onward to even longer half-lives, we would find that in order for even a single atom to be present today of a Universe-full of atoms five billion years ago, the half-life of those atoms would have to be twenty million years.

That's for a Universe-full. Actually, there could not have been that many radioactive atoms to begin with. Virtually all the atoms in the Universe are stable. It is extremely unlikely that more than one atom out of a billion was unstable to begin with (that is, after the first flush of creation had passed and short-lived atoms like Atom X had died out). If we restrict ourselves to that small proportion then in order for even one unstable atom to survive today, it must have a half-life of six hundred million years as absolute minimum.

If the half-life is greater than six hundred million years, or, preferably, much greater than that, then some of the atoms could be existing today. That answers my earlier question.

Few radioactive atoms have half-lives that long, but some do. The best known case, of course, is that of uranium. Uranium is made up of two types of atoms, uranium–238 and uranium–235. Uranium–238 is the more common of the two. Out of every thousand uranium atoms, taken at random, 993 are uranium–238 and only 7 are uranium–235.

Uranium–238 has an extremely long half-life, four and a half billion years. Uranium–235 has a shorter half-life (yet still not what one would really call short); it is a bit over seven hundred million years.

There are three other fairly common atoms (and several uncommon ones we won't mention) that fall into the same class as these uranium atoms. One is the element, thorium, which is made up of only one type of atom, thorium–232. It is even longer-lived than uranium–238. Thorium–232 has a half-life of fourteen billion years.

Then there is one of the varieties of potassium. Potassium is one of the most common elements in the Earth's crust, much more common than either uranium or thorium. It is made up largely of two kinds of atoms, potassium–39 and potassium–41, both of which are stable. One out of every ten thousand potassium atoms, however, is a third variety, which is potassium–40, and this variety is radioactive. The half-life of potassium–40 is about one and a fifth billion years.

Finally, there is rubidium. This element is much like potassium, but it is considerably rarer. Over a quarter of the atoms in rubidium, however, are a radioactive variety known as rubidium–87. This atom has the longest half-life I have yet mentioned; sixty-two billion years.

Now since we know the half-lives of these five types of atoms and since we have a figure for the age of the Universe, it is possible to calculate what percentage of the original quantity of each atom is still in existence today. The results are shown in Table III.

Naturally, the shorter the half-life, the smaller the percentage remaining today. Uranium–235, with a half-life close to the minimum allowed for survival, is well on the way toward disappearance. Five billion years ago, fully 280 out of every thousand uranium atoms were uranium–235. Now only 7 out of every thousand are.

These five kinds of atoms account for almost all the natural radioactivity of the Earth's crust. (The Earth's crust may be

TABLE III

Atom	Half-life	Out of every thousand atoms originally existing, there remain today . . .
Rubidium–87	62,000,000,000 years	950
Thorium–232	14,000,000,000 years	800
Uranium–238	4,500,000,000 years	540
Potassium–40	1,200,000,000 years	56
Uranium–235	710,000,000 years	8

defined as the ten-mile thick outermost layer of the Earth's solid surface.)

In Table IV, I present the latest data I can find for the occurrence of atoms of potassium, rubidium, thorium and uranium in the Earth's crust. Notice that potassium is by far the most common of these elements. However, it contains so few of the potassium–40 variety that there are actually fewer of those than there are of rubidium–87, which forms a larger percentage of a rarer element.

Merely the quantity of each atom, however, is not the whole story. There are over five and a half times as many rubidium–87 atoms in the Earth's crust as uranium–238 atoms, true. Yet uranium–238 atoms are breaking down at fourteen times the rate that rubidium–87 atoms are. Furthermore, while rubidium –87 ejects only a single particle before becoming stable, uranium –238 ejects no less than fourteen particles before reaching stability. For both these reasons, uranium–238 is responsible for many more of the flying sub-atomic particles that crisscross the Earth's crust than is the more common rubidium–87.

In fact, making allowance for the rate of breakdown and the number of particles ejected in the course of breakdown, we can prepare Table V. The particles can be divided into two main groups, the 'alpha particles' (comparatively heavy) and the 'beta particles' (comparatively light). Figures for both particles are given in Table V.

TABLE IV

Element	Out of every billion atoms in the Earth's crust the number of atoms of this element is . . .	Variety of atom	Out of every billion atoms in the Earth's crust the number of atoms of this variety is . . .
Potassium	13,400,000	Potassium–40	1,600
Rubidium	66,000	Ribidium–87	1,800
Thorium	1,000	Thorium–232	1,000
Uranium	320	Uranium–238	318
		Uranium–235	2

Let's look at Earth's radioactivity in another way. In the Earth's crust there are roughly 6×10^{47} atoms (a 6 followed by 47 zeros) and of these about 3×10^{42} are our five radioactive varieties. If we consider all the radioactive atoms in the entire crust, it can be calculated that the total number of sub-atomic particles being shot out of atomic nuclei in the crust amounts to 2×10^{24} (or two trillion trillion) *every second*!

Undoubtedly, this number is too big to grasp, so we'll cut it down to size. Suppose the radioactivity of the Earth's crust

TABLE V

Atom	Out of every thousand particles released by radioactive breakdown . . .	
	the number of alpha particles released is . . .	the number of beta particles released is . . .
Potassium–40	—	185
Rubidium–87	—	12
Thorium–232	195	135
Uranium–238	270	190
Uranium–235	8	5
Total	473	527

were evenly spread all over (which, of course, it isn't) and suppose you owned an acre of land. The top ten feet of your acre would weigh about 38,000 tons, and in it there would be two and a third billion particles shot out by radioactive atoms every second.

Still too big? Very well, then, consider a cubic foot of soil (about 170 pounds). If it contained its fair share of the radioactive elements, it would be bouncing to the tune of 5,000 particles ejected every second.

Despite the fact that uranium–235 is almost all gone, atoms of much shorter half-life exist on Earth. Radium, for instance. The longest-lived variety of that element, radium–226, has a half-life of only 1,622 years. This is far, far less than the six hundred millicn year minimum I set earlier as necessary for existence. Yet radium exists.

If this seems contradictory at first sight, remember that I have been supposing that atoms were created only at the time the Universe was formed. Any radium atoms that were formed then have, indeed, disappeared many eons ago. But why should we suppose that no radium atoms have been formed since the beginning of the Universe; why should we suppose that no radium atoms are being formed right now?

In fact, radioactive atoms can be formed and are being formed continuously. One natural method for producing unstable atoms in quantity involves cosmic radiation. This consists of extremely high-speed sub-atomic particles that originate from outside the Earth. They are the most energetic particles we know. They bombard Earth every second of the day and night. They plow into Earth's atmosphere and when they hit some atom in the atmosphere, that atom goes smash.

One quite interesting atomic change that takes place as a result is the conversion of occasional nitrogen atoms to an unstable variety of carbon called carbon–14. Carbon–14 has a half-life of only 5,570 years, but new formation by cosmic rays keeps pace with its breakdown and among the carbon dioxide molecules of the atmosphere, just over one carbon atom out of a trillion is carbon–14.

Cosmic radiation, however, has nothing to do with radium. To get to that, let's turn our attention again to the long-lived radioactive atoms: uranium–238, uranium–235, thorium–232, rubidium–87 and potassium–40.

Rubidium–87 and potassium–40 break down simply. Each eliminates a beta particle and is done. Having rid itself of a beta particle, the rubidium–87 atom becomes a strontium–87 atom which is stable; the potassium–40 atom becomes a calcium–40 atom which is also stable. The breakdowns are ended.

The breakdowns of uranium–238, uranium–235 and thorium –232, however, are more complicated affairs and in that complication rests the solution of our problem.

Take uranium–238, for instance. It breaks down by ejecting an alpha particle. In doing so, it forms the atom thorium–234. But thorium–234 is not stable. In fact, it is much shorter-lived than uranium–238 and has a half-life of only 24 days.

The thorium–234 atom breaks down by emitting a beta particle and becoming protactinium–234. But that is unstable, too, and has a half-life of less than seven hours. Protactinium–234 breaks down and so does the atom it becomes and the atom *it* becomes and so on. All told, uranium–238 breaks down through a total of 16 varieties of atoms before it finally becomes lead–206 (a stable atom) and comes to rest.

Uranium–235 goes through a similar process, breaking down through 13 varieties of atoms before becoming lead–207, a stable atom. Thorium–232 breaks down through 11 varieties of atoms before becoming lead–208, a stable atom.

These three series of atom varieties do not duplicate one another at any stage. Any variety of atom formed in one of the series is not formed in either of the other two. This means that a total of 40 different kinds of radioactive atoms are produced during the breakdown of uranium–238, uranium–235 and thorium–232.

All 40 descendant atoms are continually breaking down but are also continually being produced, so all 40 exist on Earth wherever uranium and thorium are found, and will exist as long as uranium and thorium do. One of the 16 kinds of radioactive atoms formed from uranium–238 during its breakdown is radium–226 and that is why radium–226 still exists on Earth and will continue to exist unless mankind consumes all Earth's uranium in nuclear power plants.

The next question is, how much of these short-lived radioactive atoms exist on Earth as a result of uranium and thorium breakdown. It turns out that the ratio of quantity of a 'descendant' atom and its 'parent' is the same as the ratio of the half-lives.

Let's take an actual case. Uranium–238 has a half-life of four and a half billion years. Thorium–234, its first descendant atom, has a half-life of 24 days. The half-life of uranium–238 is thus sixty-eight billion times as long as that of thorium–234; therefore, there is one atom of thorium–234 present in the Earth for every sixty-eight billion atoms of uranium–238. It's as straightforward as that.

Once in a while, it happens that a radioactive atom can break down in two different ways. For instance, the radioactive bismuth–212 atom (which is one of the descendants of thorium–232) can lose an alpha particle to form thallium–208, or it can lose a beta particle to form polonium–212. For every three bismuth–212 atoms that break down, one polonium–212 atom and two thallium–208 atoms are formed. Whenever such 'branching' occurs, this must also be taken into account in determining the quantity of descendant atoms present in the Earth.

When the total amounts of the various descendant atoms are calculated, it turns out that many are present in comparatively trifling amounts. Still, each of the three parent atoms, uranium–238, uranium–235 and thorium–232, has at least two descendants that do fairly well and are present in the ratio of at least one atom for every ten billion of the parent. These descendants are listed in Table VI.

As you can see, uranium–234 is the most long-lived of these descendants. It is so long-lived (with a half-life of a quarter of a million years) that it piles up in uranium–238 to the point where there is one atom of uranium–234 for every 18,000 atoms of uranium–238. In other words, there is one atom of uranium–234 for every 130 atoms of the much longer-lived uranium–235.

The total number of atoms in the Earth's crust is, as I said

TABLE VI

Atom	Half-life	For every ten billion atoms of uranium–238, there are . . .
Uranium–234	248,000 years	550,000 atoms
Thorium–230	80,000 years	175,000 atoms
Radium–226	1,622 years	3,620 atoms
Lead–210	22 years	49 atoms
		For every ten billion atoms of uranium–235, there are . . .
Protactinium–231	34,300 years	485,000 atoms
Actinium–227	22 years	310 atoms
		For every ten billion atoms of thorium–232, there are . . .
Radium–228	80 months	5 atoms
Thorium–228	20 months	1½ atoms

earlier, 6×10^{47}. From that and from other data given earlier, we can calculate the total number of atoms of uranium–238, uranium–235 and thorium–232 in the Earth's crust. Having got so far, we can then determine the number of atoms present for any of the descendants. What's more, knowing the number of atoms of any substance, it is possible to calculate the corresponding weight and that is given in Table VII.

As you see from Table VII, it turns out that through the normal processes of the radioactive breakdown of uranium–238, the supply of radium–226 in the Earth's crust amounts to over twenty-eight million tons. A ton of radium–226 (assuming it to be five times as dense as water) takes up about six and a half cubic feet. The total quantity of radium in the Earth's crust is therefore 184 million cubic feet. If this were spread evenly over an area the size of Manhattan Island (which is 22 square miles in area), it would cover it 3½ inches deep.

TABLE VII

Atom	Quantity present in the Earth's crust
Thorium–232	255,000,000,000,000 tons
Uranium–238	83,000,000,000,000 tons
Uranium–235	575,000,000,000 tons
Uranium–234	4,300,000,000 tons
Thorium–230	1,400,000,000 tons
Radium–226	28,300,000 tons
Protactinium–231	10,000,000 tons
Lead–210	545,000 tons
Radium–228	126,000 tons
Thorium–228	39,000 tons
Actinium–227	6,600 tons

Of course, far less radium is actually available to mankind. We can only dig through the topmost layers of the crust and only in certain parts of Earth's land area. At most, only one or two per cent of the crust is available to us and even there the radium–226 is spread so thinly that it is a Herculean task to scrape even a small fraction of an ounce together.

In Table VII, I considered only the long-lived parent atoms and their comparatively long-lived descendants. Even the least of the atom varieties mentioned is present in the Earth's crust in the thousands of tons. However, there are 31 varieties of descendant atoms that are not mentioned in Table VII. What of them?

To get the other end of the picture, I'll begin by listing descendant atoms with very short half-lives in Table VIII.

The half-lives of some of these atoms are so short that the second becomes an inconveniently long time interval to use as a measure. The microsecond (one-millionth of a second) is handier. It seems much more casual and neat to say that the half-life of astatine–215 is 100 microseconds than to say that it is one ten-thousandth of a second. Even a microsecond is none too small. Polonium–212 has a half-life that is only about a third of a microsecond and it isn't a record-breaking example by any means.

The short half-lives are not the only things that make the atoms listed in Table VIII rare. Most of them are formed through branched breakdowns of their parent atom, usually on the short side of the branch. For instance, thallium–206 is formed through the breakdown of bismuth–210. Bismuth –210, however, also breaks down to form polonium–210. But

TABLE VIII

Atom	Half-life
Francium–223	20 minutes
Thallium–206	4·2 minutes
Astatine–218	2 seconds
Polonium–216	0·16 seconds
Polonium–211	0·005 seconds (or 5,000 micro-seconds)
Polonium–215	0·0018 seconds (or 1,800 micro-seconds)
Astatine–216	0·0003 seconds (or 300 micro-seconds)
Polonium–214	0·00015 seconds (or 150 micro-seconds)
Astatine–215	0·00010 seconds (or 100 micro-seconds)
Polonium–212	0·0000003 seconds (or 0·3 micro-seconds)

out of every 10,000,000 bismuth–210 atoms that break down, 9,999,999 turn into polonium–210 and only 1, just 1, becomes thallium–206.

If the short half-life is taken into account and also whatever short-changing the various atoms may have had in the way of branched breakdowns, it is possible to calculate the weight of each·variety of atom present in the Earth's crust. This is done in Table IX.

You can see it is no longer a question of tons at all. Except

TABLE IX

Atom	Amount in the Earth's crust
Francium–223	10 ounces
Polonium–216	2·8 ounces
Astatine–218	0·014 ounces
Polonium–211	0·0032 ounces
Polonium–214	0·0026 ounces
Polonium–215	0·0013 ounces
Thallium–206	0·00041 ounces
Polonium–212	0·0000045 ounces
Astatine–216	0·00000073 ounces
Astatine–215	0·00000000032 ounces

for two of the atom varieties, it isn't even a question of ounces, but of fractions of ounces. Astatine–215 is worst off. Not only has it a short half-life (100 microseconds), but it is formed from uranium–235, which is the least common of the three parent atoms. To top it off, astatine–215 is at the short end of a 200,000 to 1 branching breakdown. The result is that in the entire crust of the Earth, there is less than a billionth of an ounce of astatine–215. If it were all gathered together in one spot, it wouldn't be enough to see with the naked eye.

Consider once again the acre of land ten feet deep I mentioned earlier in this chapter. That amount of soil would contain something like 10^{33} atoms (a billion trillion trillion). If all the various atoms in the Earth's crust were spread evenly throughout, you would find in your acre of land, three hundred trillion trillion atoms of uranium and one trillion trillion atoms of gold. (That's right, gold is much rarer than uranium.) There would be a little over a billion atoms even of francium–223.

The chances, however, would be 30 to 1 against there being even a single atom of astatine–215 present.

CHAPTER TWO

THE EXPLOSIONS WITHIN US

I T IS all very well to speak of radioactive atoms that occur in the soil, as I have been doing in the previous chapter. There is something objective and detached about atoms exploding within rocks and soil. But plants grow in the soil and animals live on plants. Is it possible that radioactive atoms may find their way into living tissue and even into our own bodies?

It is not only possible; it is certain.

In general, living tissue is made up of the common elements of the environment it lives in, but there are exceptions. Some very common elements play no part in the machinery of life. For instance, silicon, which is the second most common element, and aluminum, which is third, do not occur in the body. On the other hand, small quantities of moderately rare elements do occur.

In order to make some decisions about the nature of the radioactivity within the human body, then, we can't use figures based on the composition of the soil. We must know the composition of living tissue. I will therefore begin with a list of the elements that occur in living tissue and give the best estimates I can find or calculate as to the quantity of each present. You will find this in Table X.

We can leave the other elements out of consideration. The other elements *do* occur, of course. We cannot help but swallow extraneous matter with our food and are bound to get elements such as silicon and aluminum into our intestines that way. Some even manages to get absorbed into our body proper.

In fact, if we went over the body, atom by atom, we would probably find at least one atom of every variety known to exist in the soil, ocean and atmosphere of Earth. Knowledge concerning the concentration of these 'accidental' elements in the human body is still very slim, however. For the purposes of this discussion, I'll forget about them.

You might wonder, by the way, about the elements at the

TABLE X

Element	Number of atoms present for every billion atoms in the body
Hydrogen	630,000,000
Oxygen	255,000,000
Carbon	94,500,000
Nitrogen	13,500,000
Calcium	3,100,000
Phosphorus	2,200,000
Potassium	570,000
Sulfur	490,000
Sodium	410,000
Chlorine	260,000
Magnesium	130,000
Iron	38,500
Zinc	1,500
Manganese	170
Copper	170
Fluorine	125
Iodine	20
Molybdenum	10
Cobalt	5

bottom of the table, the ones that occur only to the extent of a few atoms per billion. They are usually referred to as the 'trace elements' because they are present only in traces. Does the body really need them? It certainly does. With the exception of fluorine, they are absolutely essential to human life and even fluorine is necessary for healthy teeth.

Does it seem strange to you that the body can do with so little and yet not be able to get along with none at all? From five atoms per billion to zero atoms per billion seems such a small step.

Well, it's all in the way you look at it. Suppose we count the atoms involved.

Start with a hundred and fifty pound human being. He is made up mostly, but not entirely, of microscopic cells, which are the individual chemical factories of the body. The 'not entirely' part comes about as follows: In the blood and in the spaces between the cells there is a total of some 30 pounds of fluid (mostly water) which does not form part of any cell and is called 'extracellular fluid'. In the bones and teeth there are some 15 pounds of mineral matter which is also extracellular. This leaves 105 pounds of cells.

The average liver cell weighs about one fourteenth-billionth of an ounce. Let's assume that this is about average for the weight of a cell. In that case, there are some twenty-five trillion (25,000,000,000,000) cells in the body.

The material outside the cells does not contain the same elements in the same proportion as the material inside the cells. For instance, the extracellular fluid is richer in sodium and poorer in potassium than the material inside the cells. The mineral matter in the bones is richer in calcium and phosphorus and poorer in carbon and nitrogen than the material inside the cells.

Furthermore, the cells of various tissues differ among themselves. For instance, liver cells have at least two or three times as high a concentration of copper and cobalt as do most other types of cells; red blood cells are particularly rich in iron, and so on.

Nevertheless, to begin with, I am going to suppose that the material of the body is divided up perfectly evenly among the cells and the extracellular material. Well, then, each cell contains about ninety trillion (90,000,000,000,000) atoms. Using Table X, it is easy to calculate how much of each trace element is present in each cell. The figures are given in Table XI. (I

TABLE XI

Element	Number of atoms present in each cell
Zinc	135,000,000
Manganese	15,300,000
Copper	15,300,000
Iodine	1,800,000
Molybdenum	900,000
Cobalt	450,000

leave out fluorine in that table since it is not essential to life and in its case we know for sure that it occurs only in the mineral matter of the bones and teeth and hardly at all in the cells themselves.)

So you see, even in the case of the least of these trace elements, cobalt, each individual cell, each of the little factories of the body, has nearly half a million atoms at its disposal. Actually, this is a conservative estimate for the chances are that the trace elements are more highly concentrated in the cells than in the extracellular material. If all the cobalt were in the cells, then each one would have about 650,000 cobalt atoms. Liver cells, with a higher-than-average concentration of cobalt, might even have up to a million or two cobalt atoms apiece.

Now, then, the difference between five per billion and zero per billion may not seem much; but certainly there is a vast difference between a cell having a few hundred thousand atoms and its having none at all.

Looking over the list of elements in the human body, we see at once that we can forget about uranium, thorium or any of the long-lived varieties of unstable atoms I mentioned in the previous chapter. All, that is, but one! That one is potassium–40.

The body contains 570,000 atoms of potassium in every billion of atoms generally. One out of every nine thousand atoms of potassium is potassium–40, the radioactive variety. This means that out of every billion atoms in the body, 63 are potassium–40.

This is no small amount. There is more than three times as much potassium–40 in the body as there is iodine. If potassium is considered to be spread evenly through the body, there would be, on the average, about five and a half million atoms of potassium–40 per cell. Actually, it is worse than that. Ninety-eight per cent of the body's potassium is within the cells and only two per cent is in the extracellular material. That raises the number to an even eight million atoms of potassium–40 per cell.

Fortunately, all those atoms of potassium–40 aren't breaking down simultaneously. At any time, only a comparatively small number are breaking down since potassium–40 is a long-lived atom with a half-life of over a billion years. In fact only one atom out of every fifty-three thousand trillion (53,000,000,000,000,000) atoms of potassium–40 breaks down each second.

Don't heave a sigh of relief too soon, however. In the body as a whole there is so much potassium–40 that even at this incredibly low rate of breakdown, 38,000 atoms of potassium–40 are exploding each second. In nine-tenths of the breakdowns, a beta particle is emitted. (The remaining 10 per cent of the breakdowns take another form which need not concern us here.) This means that during the course of each second, we are subjected to the effects of 35,000 beta particles crisscrossing within us. Things may seem a little better, though, if we consider the explosions in a single cell rather than in the body as a whole. Each particular cell undergoes one of these explosions, on the average, only once every two hundred years.

Or, to put it still more comfortingly, if you live for seventy years, then the odds are two to one that any particular cell of your body will never know what it is to have a potassium–40 atom explode within it.

Well, how do these explosions affect us? Obviously, they don't kill us outright. We're not even aware of them.

Yet they have the capacity for damage. Enough radioactivity can kill and *has* killed, but 35,000 explosions per second are far from enough to do that. What about milder effects, though? A beta particle, as it darts out of a breaking down potassium–40 atom usually hits a water molecule (which is by far the most common molecule in the body) and knocks off a piece of it. What is left of the water molecule is called a 'free radical'. Free radicals are reactive substances that will tear into any molecule they come across.

There is always a chance, then, that the unfortunate molecule that finds itself in the path of a free radical may be one of the nucleo-protein molecules called 'genes'. There are several thousand genes in each cell, each gene controlling some particular facet of the cell's chemistry. If one of those genes is damaged or altered as a result of a collision with a free radical, the cell's chemistry is also altered to some extent. The same thing happens, of course, if the beta particle should happen to hit the gene directly.

If the cells whose chemistry is altered happen to be germ cells (that is, cells which eventually give rise to ova or spermatozoa—as the case may be), it is quite possible that the offspring of the organism exposed will end up with a chemical organization different from that of its parents. The change may be so small and unimportant as to be completely unnoticeable, or sufficiently great as to cause physical deformity or early death. In either case the change is referred to as a 'mutation'.

If a gene is changed in a cell other than a germ cell; the cell may be altered with no permanent hardship to the body as a whole, or (just possibly) it may be converted to a cancerous cell with very drastic results.

This is not just speculation. Animals exposed to high-energy radioactive particles or to radiation energetic enough to be capable of manhandling genes, may be damaged to the extent of developing radiation sickness and dying. At lower doses, the animals will show an increased incidence of cancer and of mutations.

Nor are human beings immune. Radioactive radiations and X-rays have caused cancer in human beings and killed them, too. Some skin cancers have been attributed to over-exposure to the sun's ultra-violet radiation.

But when all known causes of cancer and mutations are eliminated there always remain a certain number that seem 'spontaneous'; that arise from no known cause.

Well, then, the thought arises, or should arise—can these 'spontaneous' cases be due to the potassium–40 beta particles careering around within us all. This has been thought of, to be sure, and chemists have calculated the probabilities of beta particles (or free radicals produced by them) just happening to strike a gene and damaging it.

The results of these calculations seem conclusive. The effect is insufficient! The radiation to which a human being is subjected as a result of potassium–40 atoms within him is about the same as the radiation to which he is exposed as a result of cosmic ray bombardment from outer space. Both together cannot possibly account for more than a tiny fraction of the 'spontaneous' cancers and mutations.

But are we through? Have we exhausted the possibilities of explosions within us?

The answer is 'No' to both questions. In the last chapter, I mentioned that the bombardment of the atmosphere by cosmic rays results in the continuous production of carbon–14. Carbon–14 is radioactive and has a half-life of only 5,570 years, but its presence is maintained at an even level by cosmic-ray production at a rate that just balances its rate of breakdown.

This 'even level' is certainly not very high. Carbon atoms exist in the atmosphere as part of the molecules of the gaseous substance, carbon dioxide. Only 0·04 per cent of the atmosphere is carbon dioxide. Only one of the three atoms in the carbon dioxide molecule is carbon. And only one carbon atom out of every eight hundred billion (800,000,000,000) is carbon–14. Certainly, the total amount of carbon–14 present in the atmosphere doesn't seem to be overwhelming. Let's see!

The weight of the atmosphere is 14·7 pounds on every square inch of the Earth's surface. Take into account all the square inches there are on the Earth's surface (a little over eight hundred thousand trillion (800,000,000,000,000,000) if you're curious) and the total weight of the atmosphere turns out to be five thousand nine hundred trillion (5,900,000,000,000,000) tons.

From this we see that the total weight of carbon dioxide in the atmosphere is two trillion three hundred and sixty billion (2,360,000,000,000) tons; the total weight of the carbon atoms themselves is seven hundred and fifty billion (750,000,000,000) tons; and the total weight of the carbon–14 is 0·9 tons, or 1,800 pounds. Indeed, not an overwhelming amount, but then not an insignificant one either.

Eighteen hundred pounds of carbon–14 contain thirty-five thousand trillion trillion (35,000,000,000,000,000,000,000,000,000) atoms. If these are spread evenly through the atmosphere, each cubic inch of air (at room temperature and sea-level pressure) would contain 120,000 atoms of carbon–14. In the air contained in a moderately-sized living-room there would be over three hundred billion atoms of carbon–14.

Put it another way. Every time you breathe, 30 cubic inches of air moves in and out of your lungs. That means that each time you breathe, you pump three and a half million atoms of carbon–14 into your lungs. In an average lifetime, you will have breathed over two thousand trillion atoms of carbon–14.

Not insignificant at all!

But do any of these atoms become part of living tissue? They certainly do; that is the crux of the whole thing.

Living matter is approximately 10 per cent carbon by weight. Every bit of that carbon, whether the organism is large or microscopic, plant or animal, of the sea or of the land, came originally from the carbon dioxide of the air. Green plants incorporate carbon dioxide of the air into larger carbon-containing molecules. (Microscopic plants in the ocean may use carbon dioxide molecules that have dissolved in the sea and reacted with the water molecules found therein, but that came originally from the air, too.) Animals eat the plants (or other animals that have already eaten the plants) and use the carbon atoms as hand-me-downs for their own purposes.

Since living tissue makes no distinction (or practically none) between carbon–14, which is radioactive, and carbon–12 and carbon–13, both of which are stable, the proportion of carbon–14 in living matter, including your own personal living matter, is the same as it is in air.

As long as you (or any living creature) is alive, the proportion of carbon–14 in your body remains constant. You remain in constant balance with the atmosphere where the production of carbon–14 by cosmic rays just balances its rate of breakdown. The result is that carbon isolated from any recently living object contains enough carbon–14 to cause the liberation of 450 beta particles a minute for every ounce of carbon present.

In the last ten years or so, this fact has become important to archeologists.

You see, as soon as an organism dies, it stops incorporating carbon dioxide (either directly from the atmosphere or in- directly, by way of its food) into its tissues. Therefore, it stops collecting carbon–14. Whatever carbon–14 was in its tissues at the moment of its death remains, but that slowly breaks down. At the end of 5,570 years, the carbon–14 of its remains is half gone. Carbon isolated from those remains would produce only 225 beta particles per minute per ounce.

It is fairly easy to count the beta particle production, using appropriate devices, and so we have a method for telling how old any object of living origin might be. The age of a mummy might be told from the 'counts' given off by his mummified flesh or by his linen wrappings. The wood of some old prehistoric Indian abode or some ancient parchment could be tested.

This method of 'radiocarbon dating' is quite objective and doesn't depend upon anyone's historical theories or anyone's interpretation of ancient inscriptions. It has been used to estimate the time when mankind first arrived in the Western Hemisphere. By and large, its results have been in accord with decisions previously reached by historians.

To get an idea how the number of counts correlates with age, look at Table XII.

TABLE XII

Number of counts per ounce of carbon	Age in years of the specimen
450	—
400	900
350	2,000
300	3,250
250	4,700
225	5,570
200	6,500
175	7,600
150	8,800
125	10,400
100	12,100
75	14,500
50	17,500
25	23,000
15	27,300
10	30,500
5	36,000

Naturally, the fewer the counts, the more chance there is of error. All mathematical treatment of radioactive breakdown is statistical in nature and statistics works more poorly as numbers grow smaller. By the time you get down to just a few counts per ounce, you're on rocky ground. Furthermore, there are always stray counts coming from radioactive atoms of all sorts that happen to be close at hand. This is called 'background radiation'. The amount of this is small, but as the carbon–14 counts get fewer and fewer, even a small amount of background radiation can throw results badly awry. For these reasons, radiocarbon dating has its limitations and can only be pushed back in time (with increasing shakiness) some thirty thousand years.

But we mustn't stay away from our main subject too long. What about the effects of the carbon–14 in our body?

The hundred and fifty pound man I mentioned earlier in the article contains about three hundred trillion trillion (300,000,000,000,000,000,000,000,000) carbon atoms. Of these, some three hundred and fifty trillion (350,000,000,000,000) are carbon–14 atoms. If we omit the mineral matter of the body, and assume the carbon–14 atoms are spread out evenly otherwise, then each cell contains just about 11 atoms of carbon–14.

This is quite a small figure when you compare it with even the rarest trace element in the body. There are 40,000 times as many cobalt atoms in a cell, at the very least, as carbon–14 atoms. The comparison with potassium–40 is even more extreme. There are over 700,000 times as many potassium–40 atoms in a cell as carbon–14.

If it has been decided, then, that potassium–40 is quite harmless to the body, it would certainly seem as though carbon–14 ought to be harmless thousands of times more emphatically.

But wait! Carbon–14 has a much shorter half-life than has potassium–40. An equivalently larger proportion of its atoms ought to be breaking down per second, and after all it is the number of beta particles being produced, and not the number of atoms, that counts.

Well, knowing the number of carbon–14 atoms present and the half-life of carbon–14, we can calculate that each second there are some twelve hundred beta particles produced within the body by carbon–14 breakdowns.

The proportion of potassium–40 is still greater, but no longer so one-sidedly. Potassium–40 produces nearly 30 times as many beta particles as does carbon–14.

But there is another point that must be considered, though, in addition to mere numbers. The energy of the beta particles produced by potassium–40 is some ten times as great as those produced by carbon–14. The potassium–40 atom, as it breaks down, can therefore do ten times the damage that carbon–14 atoms can do as they explode. That swings the pendulum in the other direction again, for it would now appear that potassium–40 in the body does, on the whole, 300 times the damage carbon–14 does.

Certainly, it seems that no matter what we do, or how we slice it, carbon–14 remains badly out of the running.

Ah, but carbon–14 has a trump up its sleeve!

The key molecules of the cells are the genes I mentioned earlier. It is change in these which can bring about mutations and cancer. These genes contain no potassium atoms in their molecule. Any potassium–40 atoms present in the cell are located elsewhere than in the gene. Beta particles that shoot out of an exploding potassium–40 atom must strike a gene molecule just right or must give rise to a free radical which will strike it just right. It is as though you were standing in a globular shooting gallery, blindfolded, and aimed at random in the hope of hitting a few tiny targets placed here and there on the walls, floor and ceiling.

All in all, the chances of a beta particle from a potassium–40 atom doing damage to a gene, either directly or indirectly, is very low; perhaps only one out of many millions.

But now let's consider carbon–14. The gene is not merely being shot at by beta particles from exploding carbon–14 atoms. It *contains* carbon–14 atoms.

The genes make up about 1 per cent of the average cell. (Only of the cells now; there are no genes in the extracellular material.) This means there are some twenty-four trillion trillion atoms in the genes of which half, or twelve trillion trillion (12,000,000,000,000,000,000,000,000) are carbon atoms.

Of these, some fourteen trillion (14,000,000,000,000) are carbon–14 atoms.

It comes to this, then: There is, on the average, one carbon–14 atom in the genes of every two cells.

The number of these that break down can be calculated. It turns out that each second, in your body as a whole, 50 carbon–14 atoms, *located in the genes*, are exploding and sending out a beta particle. These may be weaker and fewer than the beta particles sent out by exploding potassium–40 molecules, but every one of these fifty scores a hit!

Even if you suppose that the beta particle from an exploding carbon–14 atom within a gene might plow through the remainder of the gene without hitting any of its atoms squarely enough to do damage (this is possible) the fact still remains that the exploded carbon–14 atom has been converted to a stable nitrogen–14 atom. By this change of carbon to nitrogen, the gene is chemically altered (only slightly perhaps, but altered nevertheless). Furthermore, the carbon–14 atom, having shot out a beta particle, recoils just as a rifle would when it shoots out a bullet. This recoil may break it away from its surrounding atoms in the molecule and this introduces another change, and an even more important one.

In order for potassium–40 to do as much damage to a gene as the gene's own carbon–14 will do, the chances of a beta particle from a potassium–40 atom (or its free radical product) striking a gene hard enough to do damage must be at least as good as one in eight thousand. The chances just aren't that high or anything like it, so I end by concluding that carbon–14 is much more likely to be responsible for 'spontaneous' cancer and mutations than potassium–40 is.

And if that is so, there is precious little that can be done about it unless someone turns off the cosmic rays, or unless we build underground cities.

However, the situation isn't as serious as you might think. Fifty explosions per second within your genes may sound as though you couldn't last very long without developing cancer or having deformed children, but remember, a change in a gene may mean any kind of a change whatever. In the vast majority of cases, any serious change (and we don't really know how big a change must be before it's 'serious') simply results in that particular gene in that particular cell refusing to work at all. Probably only a vanishingly small percentage of the changes result in cancer. (And if we only knew what the details of *that* change was!)

Then again, some cells are more important than others. Only the cells that give rise to ova and spermatozoa can be responsible for mutated children, and they form only a small percentage of the total number of cells in the body.

Fifty explosions per second over the entire body doesn't mean much to the individual cell (any more than the fact that twenty stars in our Galaxy blow up each year should cause us to worry much about our Sun). If you were to consider a single particular cell in the body, chosen at random, then an average of 18,000 *years* must pass before a single carbon–14 explodes in its genes.

This is the same as saying that if you live to be 70, the chances that a particular cell in your body will ever have experienced even a single carbon–14 breakdown in its genes is only one in 260.

So sleep in comfort!

CHAPTER THREE

HEMOGLOBIN AND THE UNIVERSE

EVEN the purest and most high-minded scientist finds it expedient sometimes to assault the fortress of truth with the blunt weapon of trial and error. Sometimes it works beautifully. As evidence and as a case in point, let us bring to the front of the stage the hemoglobin molecule.

Hemoglobin is the chief protein component of the red blood cells. It has the faculty of loosely combining with molecular oxygen to form oxyhemoglobin. That combination takes place in the small blood vessels of the lungs. The oxyhemoglobin there formed is carried by the blood stream to all the cells of the body; it gives up its oxygen to these cells and becomes hemoglobin once more. It is then ready to make its way to the lungs for another load.

Because of hemoglobin's vital function in life and because of its ready availability in fairly pure form, the protein has been subjected to the closest scrutiny on the part of chemists. It was found, for instance, that the hemoglobin molecule is approximately a parallelepiped in shape, with dimensions of 6·4 by 4·8 by 3·6 millimicrons. (A millimicron is one-billionth of a meter; a meter is forty inches.) The bulk of this molecule is 'globin' which, by itself, is an unstable protein. It makes up 97 per cent of the whole. Attached to the globin, and rendering the whole more stable, are four iron-bearing groups called 'heme' (*see Figure* 1).

Hemoglobin can be split apart into a heme fraction and a globin fraction without very much difficulty, and the two can be studied separately. Heme, being simpler in construction and quite stable in addition, has been naturally the more intensively investigated of the two.

The heme molecule is flat and approximately circular in shape. In the very center of heme is an iron atom. Surrounding that iron atom are twenty carbon atoms and four nitrogen

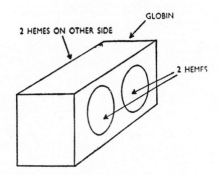

Figure 1. Schematic representation of hemoglobin molecule.

atoms—plus some hydrogens—arranged in four small rings that are themselves connected into one big ring. This wheels within wheels arrangement occurs in numerous compounds other than heme—notably in chlorophyll—and is called the 'porphyrin ring'. Establishing the structure of the porphyrin ring itself took some fancy footwork, but was a relatively straightforward matter.

Now, however, there enters an additional refinement. There are eight points in the porphyrin ring where groups of atoms called 'side-chains' can be, and are, attached. In the heme molecule, the eight side-chains are of three varieties: four of one kind, two of another, and two of a third. Porphyrin rings to which are attached that particular combination of side-chains are called 'protoporphyrins'.

Now this is the ticklish point. Which side-chains are attached to which positions in the porphyrin ring? To illustrate the difficulty, let's draw some pictures. Since this chapter concerns itself not with chemistry—despite appearances so far—but merely with some simple arithmetic, there is no need to make an accurate representation of the porphyrin ring. It will be sufficient to draw a ticktacktoe design (*Figure* 2). Topologically, we have achieved all that is necessary. The two ends of each of the four lines represent the eight positions to which side-chains can be attached.

If we symbolize the side-chains as *a*, *b*, and *c* (four *a*'s, two *b*'s, and two *c*'s), several arrangements can be represented. Two of these are shown in *Figures* 3*a* and 3*b*. Altogether fifteen

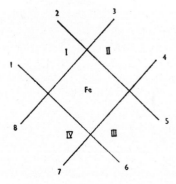

Figure 2. Schematic representation of heme molecule. (Note: The positions available for side-chain attachment are numbered 1 to 8. The small rings which are themselves combined to form the porphyrin ring are numbered I to IV. The symbol Fe stands for the iron atom.)

different and distinct arrangements can exist. Each arrangement represents a molecule with properties that are in some respects different from those of the molecules represented by every other arrangement. Only one of the fifteen is *the* arrangement found in heme.

Which one?

A German chemist, Hans Fischer, was faced with that

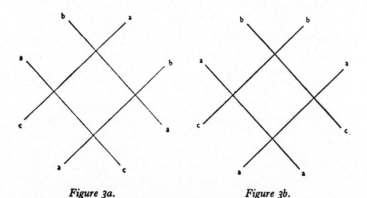

Figure 3a.   Figure 3b.

*Two possible arrangements of protoporphyrin side-chains.
(Note: The reader may think he can draw more arrangements than the fifteen stated in the text to be the number that can exist. So he can! However, the porphyrin ring possesses four-fold radial symmetry and front-back bilateral symmetry which reduces the number of different arrangements eightfold. Furthermore, certain arrangements could be ruled out for various chemical reasons. There remain, as stated, fifteen arrangements in all which cannot be ruled out either by symmetry or by chemical reasoning.)*

problem and he solved it in the most straightforward possible manner. He wrote down the fifteen possible arrangements on pieces of paper, numbering them arbitrarily from one to fifteen. He then, in effect, called out sixty graduate students, separated them into platoons of four apiece, and gave each platoon one of the arrangements. Instructions were for each to synthesize the protoporphyrin with the particular arrangement pictured.

The students got to work. As each protoporphyrin was formed, its properties were compared with those of the natural protoporphyrin obtained from hemoglobin. It turned out that only one of the synthetic protoporphyrins matched the natural product. It was the one that Fischer had happened to assign the number 9, and it has the side-chain arrangement shown in

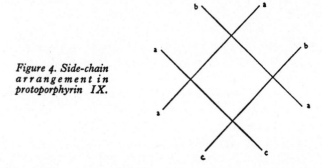

Figure 4. Side-chain arrangement in protoporphyrin IX.

Figure 4. Since then, generations of medical students and biochemists have memorized the formula of the natural product and learned to call it 'Protoporphyrin IX'. (It is my personal experience that few students show any curiosity at all as to why the IX.)

Score a tremendous victory for pure trial and error!

Now let's tackle the globin portion of the hemoglobin molecule. Globin is, as has been said, protein in nature, and proteins are by far the most important chemicals in living tissue. There is no question but that most or all of the secrets of life lie hidden in the details of protein structure. A biochemist who could learn the exact structure of some protein would be an awfully happy biochemist. So let's get some notion as to what it would take to achieve that desirable end.

All protein molecules are made up of relatively small compounds called 'amino-acids', which are strung together in the molecule like beads on a string. There are about twenty different amino-acids occurring in proteins and the structure of each one of them is exactly known. Furthermore, the exact manner in which amino-acids are hooked together in a chain to form a protein molecule is also known. Finally, in the case of many proteins, including hemoglobin, we know exactly how many of each amino-acid the molecule contains. Most of the problem seems to be solved. The main thing left is to figure out the exact order in which the different amino-acids occur along the protein chain.

To show what I mean, let's suppose we have a very small protein molecule made up of four different amino-acids: *a*, *b*, *c*, and *d*. These four amino-acids can be arranged in twenty-four different ways, as shown in *Figure 5*. Each arrangement represents a molecule with distinct properties of its own. The situation is then similar to that in the case of heme. Each of the twenty-four possible molecules can be synthesized and its properties compared with the natural product. One of the twenty-four *must* be the right one.

To be sure, hemoglobin has somewhat more than four amino-acids in its molecule so the number of possible arrangements is to be expected to be somewhat more than twenty-four. Still, proteins are so important that biochemists would be willing to go to an unusual amount of effort to solve the problem of their structure and the mere presence of additional arrangements might not discourage them. Trial and error might be a little more tedious than in the case of heme, but, given time enough, it ought to be as sure as death and taxes.

a-b-c-d-	b-a-c-d-	c-b-a-d-	d-b-c-a-
a-b-d-c-	b-a-d-c-	c-b-d-a-	d-b-a-c-
a-c-b-d-	b-c-a-d-	c-a-b-d-	d-c-b-a-
a-c-d-b-	b-c-d-a-	c-a-d-b-	d-c-a-b-
a-d-b-c-	b-d-a-c-	c-d-b-a-	d-a-b-c-
a-d-c-b-	b-d-c-a-	c-d-a-b-	d-a-c-b-

Figure 5. The different arrangements of four amino-acids in a protein chain.

Or should it?

To begin with, hemoglobin is a protein of only average size. Its molecule is made up of five hundred and thirty-nine amino-acids of exactly twenty different varieties and the number of each amino-acid present is known. There is no need to name each amino-acid. We can accomplish all that is necessary for our purposes by lettering them from *a* to *t* inclusive. There are seventy-five amino-acids of type *a* present in the molecule, fifty-four of type *b*, fifty of type *c* and so on. One possible arrangement of the five hundred and thirty-nine amino-acids is shown in *Figure* 6.

a-b-c-d-e-f-g-h-i-j-k-l-m-n-o-p-q-r-s-t-a-b-c-d-e-f-g-h-i-j- k- l- m- n- o- p- q-
r-s-a-b-c-d-e-f-g-h-i-j-k-l-m-n-o-p-q-r-s-a-b-c-d-e-f-g-h-i- j- k- l- m- n- o- p-
q-r-a-b-c-d-e-f-g-h-i-j-k-l-m-n-o-p-q-a-b-c-d-e-f- g- h- i- j- k- l- m- n- o- p-a-
b-c-d-e-f-g-h-i-j-k-l-m-n-o-p-a-b-c-d-e-f-g-h-i-j-k-l-m-n-o-p-a-b- c- d- e- f-
g-h-i-j-k-l-m-n-o-p-a-b-c-d-e-f-g-h-i-j-k-l-m-n-o-p-a-b-c-d-e-f- g- h- i- l- k-
l-m-n-o-p-a-b-c-d-e-f-g-h-i-j-k-l-m-n-o-a-b-c-d-e-f-g-h-i-j-k-l-m-n-o-a-b-
c-d-e-f-g-h-i-j-k-l-m-n-o-a-b-c-d-e-f-g-h-i-j-k-l-m-n-a-b-c-d-e-f-g-h-i-j-k-
l-m-n-a-b-c-d-e-f-g-h-i-j-k-l-m-n-a-b-c-d-e-f-g-h-i-j-k-l-m-n-a-b- c- d- e- f-
g-h-i-j-k-l-a-b-c-d-e-f-g-h-i-j-k-l-a-b-c-d-e-f-g-h-i-j-k-a-b-c-d- e- f- g- h- i- j-
k-a-b-c-d-e-f-g-h-l-j-a-b-c-d-e-f-g-h-i-j-a-b-c-d-e-f-g-h-i-a-b-c-d-e-f-g-h-i-
a-b-c-d-e-f-g-h-i-a-b-c-d-e-f-g-h-i-a-b-c-d-e-f-g-h-i-a-b-c-d-e-f-g-h- i- a- b-
c-d-e-f-g-h-a-b-c-d-e-f-g-h-a-b-c-d-e-f-g-h-a-b-c-d-e-f-g-a-b-c- d- e- f- g-a-
b-c-d-e-f-a-b-c-d-e-a-b-c-d-e-a-b-c-d-a-b-c-d-a-b-c- d- a-
b-c-d-a-b-c-d-a-b-c-d-a-b-c-d-a-b-c-d-a-b-c-a-b-c-a-b-a-b-a- b- a- b- a- a- a-
a-a-a-a-a-a-a-a-a-a-a-a-a-a-a-a-a-

Figure 6. One possible arrangement of the amino-acids in the hemo-globin molecule.

Obviously the letters in *Figure* 6 can be written down in quite a few different arrangements and the reader may well shiver a bit at the thought of trying to write down all possible combinations and then counting them. Fortunately, we don't have to do that. The number of combinations can be calculated indirectly from the data we already have.

Thus, if we have *n* different objects, then the number of ways in which they can be arranged in a line is equal to the product of all the integers from *n* down to 1. The number of combinations of four objects, for instance, is: 4 x 3 x 2 x 1, or 24. This is the number we found by actually writing out all the different combinations (*see Figure* 5). The product of all the integers from *n* to 1 is called 'factorial *n*' and is symbolized as *n*!

a-a-*-b-b*	b-a-a*-b*	
a-a*-b*-b	b-a-b*-a*	a-a-b-b
a-b-a*-b*	b-a*-a-b*	
a-b-b*-a*	b-a*-b*-a	a-b-a-b
a-b*-a*-b	b-b*-a-a*	
a-b*-b-a*	b-b*-a*-a	a-b-b-a
a*-a-b-b*	b*-a-a*-b	b-a-a-b
a*-a-b*-b	b*a-b-a*	
a*-b-a-b*	b*-b-a-a*	b-a-b-a
a*-b-b*-a	b*-b-a*-a	
a*-b*-a-b	b*-a*-a-b	b-b-a-a
a*-b*-b-a	b*-a*-b-a	

Figure 7a. The total arrangements of four amino-acids, two of one kind and two of another.

Figure 7b. The different arrangements of four amino-acids, two of one kind and two of another.

If the *n* objects are not all different, an additional complication is introduced. Suppose that our very small four-amino-acid protein is made up of two amino-acids of one kind and two of another. Let's symbolize the amino-acids as *a*, *a**, *b* and *b**. The twenty-four theoretical combinations are presented in *Figure 7a*. But if *a* and *a** are indistinguishable, and *b* and *b** likewise, then the combination *ab** is identical, for all practical purposes, with *a*b*, *a*b**, and *ab*. The combination *aba*b** is identical with *a*bab**, *ab*a*b* and so on. The total number of *different* combinations among those found in *Figure 7a* is shown in *Figure 7b*, in which asterisks are eliminated. You will note that the number of different combinations is six.

The formula for obtaining the number of different combinations of *n* objects of which the number *p* are of one kind, *q* of another, *r* of another, and so on, involves a division of factorials, thus:

$$\frac{n!}{p! \times q! \times r! \dots}$$

In the case we have just cited—that is, the four-amino-acid protein with two amino-acids of one type and two of another—the formula is:

$$\frac{4!}{2! \times 2!} \text{ or } \frac{4 \times 3 \times 2 \times 1}{2 \times 1 \times 2 \times 1} \text{ or } 6$$

Of course, the factorials involved in calculating the number of amino-acid combinations in hemoglobin are larger. We must start with factorial 539—the total number of amino acids in hemoglobin—and divide that by the product of factorial 75, factorial 54, factorial 50 and so on—the number of each amino-acid present.

The factorials of the lower integers are easy enough to calculate (*see Figure* 8). Unfortunately they build up rather rapidly. Would you make a quick guess at the value of factorial 20? You're probably wrong. The answer is approximately twenty-four hundred quadrillion, which, written in figures, is 2,400,000,000,000,000,000. And factorial values continue mounting at an ever-increasing rate.

1!	equals	1	equals 1
2!	equals	2 x 1	equals 2
3!	equals	3 x 2 x 1	equals 6
4!	equals	4 x 3 x 2 x 1	equals 24
5!	equals	5 x 4 x 3 x 2 x 1	equals 120
6!	equals	6 x 5 x 4 x 3 x 2 x 1	equals 720
7!	equals	7 x 6 x 5 x 4 x 3 x 2 x 1	equals 5040
8!	equals	8 x 7 x 6 x 5 x 4 x 3 x 2 x 1	equals 40320

Figure 8. The factorials of the first few integers.

In handling large numbers of this sort, recourse is had to exponentials of the form 10^n. 10^n is a short way of representing a numeral consisting of 1 followed by n zeros. 1,000 would be 10^3 and 1,000,000,000,000 would be 10^{12} and so on. A number like 2,500 which is in between 1,000 (that is 10^3) and 10,000 (that is 10^4) could be expressed as 10 to a fractional exponent somewhere in between 3 and 4. More often, it is written simply as $2\cdot5 \times 10^3$ (that is, $2\cdot5 \times 1,000$—which, obviously, works out to 2,500).

Written exponentially, then, factorial 20 is about $2\cdot4 \times 10^{18}$.

For the purposes of this chapter, there are several things that must be kept in mind with regard to exponential numbers:

(1) In multiplying two exponential numbers, the exponents are *added*. Thus, the product of 2×10^4 and 3×10^5 equals 6×10^9. If you translate the first two numbers to 20,000 and 300,000, you will see that the product is indeed 6,000,000,000.

(2) A number like 2,560,000 can be expressed as 256×10^4, or $25 \cdot 6 \times 10^5$ or $2 \cdot 56 \times 10^6$ or $0 \cdot 256 \times 10^7$. All are the same number, as you can see if you multiply 256 by 10,000; $25 \cdot 6$ by 100,000; $2 \cdot 56$ by 1,000,000; or $0 \cdot 256$ by 10,000,000. Which one of these exponential numbers is it best to use? It is customary to use the one in which the non-exponential portion of the number is between 1 and 10. In the case of 2,560,000, the usual exponential figure is $2 \cdot 56 \times 10^6$. For this reason, in multiplying 2×10^4 by 6×10^5, we present the answer *not* as 12×10^9, but as $1 \cdot 2 \times 10^{10}$. (Where the number 10^{10} is presented by itself, it is the same as writing 1×10^{10}.)

(3) The appearance of exponential numbers may be deceiving. 10^3 is ten times greater than 10^2. Similarly, 10^{69} is ten times greater than 10^{68}, despite the fact that intuitively they look about the same. Again, it must be remembered that 10^{12}, for instance, is not twice as great as 10^6, but a *million* times as great.

And now we are ready to return to our factorials. If factorial 20 is $2 \cdot 4 \times 10^{18}$, you may well hesitate to try to calculate the value of such numbers as factorial 50, factorial 54, factorial 75 and, above all, factorial 539. Fortunately, there exist tables of the lower factorials—say, to factorial 100—and equations whereby the higher factorials can be approximately determined.

Using both tables and equations, the number of combinations possible in hemoglobin can be computed. The answer turns out to be 4×10^{619}. If you want to see what that number looks like written out in full, see *Figure* 9. Let's agree to call 4×10^{619} the 'hemoglobin number'. Those of you, by the way, who have read Kasner and Newman's *Mathematics and the Imagination* will see that the hemoglobin number is larger than a googol (10^{100}) but smaller than a googolplex (10^{googol}).

Of all the hemoglobin number of combinations, only *one* combination has the precise properties of the hemoglobin molecule found in the human being. To test that number of combinations one after the other to find *the* one would, as you probably rightly suspect, take time. But given enough time, enough scientists, enough generations of scientists, surely trial and error would come through with the answer, inevitably, at

40,000,000,000,000,000,000,000,000,000,000,000,000,000,000,000,000,
000,000,000,000,000,000,000,000,000,000,000,000,000,000,000,000,000,
000,000,000,000,000,000,000,000,000,000,000,000,000,000,000,000,000,
000,000,000,000,000,000,000,000,000,000,000,000,000,000,000,000,000,
000,000,000,000,000,000,000,000,000,000,000,000,000,000,000,000,000,
000,000,000,000,000,000,000,000,000,000,000,000,000,000,000,000,000,
000,000,000,000,000,000,000,000,000,000,000,000,000,000,000,000,000,
000,000,000,000,000,000,000,000,000,000,000,000,000,000,000,000,000,
000,000,000,000,000,000,000,000,000,000,000,000,000,000,000,000,000,
000,000,000,000,000,000,000,000,000,000,000,000,000,000,000,000,000,
000,000,000,000,000,000,000,000,000,000,000,000,000,000,000,000,000,
000,000,000,000,000,000,000,000,000,000,000,000,000,000,000,000,000,
000,000.

Figure 9. The hemoglobin number.

long, long last. But exactly how much space and time would be required?

In order to answer that question we must first get an idea of the size of the hemoglobin number. It seems awfully big, so we'll begin by taking something grandiose as a comparison. For instance, how does the hemoglobin number compare with the total number of molecules of hemoglobin on Earth? That's a fair beginning.

The human population of the Earth is 2,500,000,000 or, exponentially, $2 \cdot 5 \times 10^9$. The average human being, including men, women and children, weighs, let us say, one hundred and twenty pounds, which is equal to $5 \cdot 5 \times 10^4$ grams. (There are 454 grams in a pound.) The total number of grams of living human flesh, blood, and bone on Earth is, therefore, about $1 \cdot 4 \times 10^{14}$ grams.

Seven per cent of the human body is blood so that the total amount of blood on Earth is $9 \cdot 0 \times 10^9$ liters. (Since a liter is equal to about $1 \cdot 06$ quarts, that figure comes to nine and a half billion quarts.) Every liter of blood contains five trillion (5×10^{12}) red cells, so the total number of human red cells on Earth is, therefore, $4 \cdot 5 \times 10^{22}$.

Although the red cell is microscopic in size, there is still enough room in each red cell for nearly three hundred million hemoglobin molecules—$2 \cdot 7 \times 10^8$, to be more precise. There are thus, on all the Earth, 10^{31} human hemoglobin molecules.

But those are the hemoglobin molecules belonging to human beings only. Other vertebrates, from whales to shrews, also possess hemoglobin in their blood, as do some lower forms of life. Let's be generous and assume that for every human hemoglobin molecule on Earth there are one billion (10^9) nonhuman hemoglobin molecules. In that case, the total number of hemoglobin molecules on Earth, human and nonhuman, is 10^{40}.

Even this number, unfortunately, is nowhere near the hemoglobin number and so it will not serve as a comparison.·

Let us bring in the element of time and see if that helps us out. The average red blood cell has a life expectancy of about one third of a year. After that it is broken up and a new red blood cell takes its place. Let us suppose that every time a new red blood cell is formed, it contains a completely new set of hemoglobin molecules. In one year, then, a total of 3×10^{40} hemoglobin molecules will have existed.

But the Earth has existed in solid state for something like three and a third billion years—3.3×10^9. Suppose that in all that time, Earth has been just as rich in hemoglobins as it is now. If that were true, the total number of hemoglobin molecules ever to have existed on Earth would be 10^{50}. This is still nowhere near the hemoglobin number.

Well, then, let us stop fooling around with one dinky little planet and its history. We have all of space and time at our disposal and as numerical enthusiasts we ought to have no qualms about using it.

It is estimated that there are one hundred billion stars in the galaxy and at least that many galaxies in the universe. Let's be generous. Let's never stint in our generosity. Let's suppose that there are a trillion stars in the galaxy, rather than merely a hundred billion. Let us suppose there are a trillion galaxies in the universe. The total number of stars in the universe would then be $10^{12} \times 10^{12}$ or 10^{24}.

Suppose now that every star—every single star—possessed in its gravitational field no less than ten planets, each one of which was capable of holding as much life as Earth can and that each one was as rich in hemoglobin. There would then be 10^{25} such planets in existence and in one year, the number of hemoglobin molecules that would have existed on all those planets—assuming always a life-expectancy of a third of a year for each molecule—would be 3×10^{65}.

Now let us suppose that each of these planets remained that rich in hemoglobin for, from first to last, three hundred billion years—3 x 10^{77}. This is a very generous figure, really, since the sun's life expectancy is only about ten to twenty billion years, during only a portion of which time will life on Earth be possible. And this life expectancy is rather longer than average for other stars, too.

Still, with all the generous assumptions we have been making, all the hemoglobin molecules that could possibly exist in all the space and time we have any knowledge of—and more—comes out to 10^{77}. This number is still virtually zero compared to the hemoglobin number.

Let's try a different tack altogether. Let's build a computing machine—a *big* computing machine. The whole known universe is estimated to be a billion light-years in diameter, so let us imagine a computing machine in the form of a cube *ten* billion light-years on each edge. If such a machine were hollow, there would be room in it for one thousand universes such as ours, including all the stars and galaxies and all the space between the various stars and galaxies as well.

Now let us suppose that the computing machine was completely filled from edge to edge and from top to bottom with tiny computing units, each one of which could test different combinations of hemoglobin amino-acids in order to see whether it was *the* hemoglobin combination or not. In order to make sure that the computing units are as numerous as possible, let's suppose that each one is no larger than the least voluminous object known, the single neutrino.

How many computing units would the machine contain?

A neutrino is a ten-billion-trillionth of a centimeter in diameter. One cubic centimeter—which is equal to only one-sixteenth of a cubic inch—will, therefore, contain 10^{21} x 10^{21} x 10^{21} or 10^{63} neutrinos, if these were packed in as tightly as possible. (We assume the neutrinos to be tiny cubes rather than tiny spheres, for simplicity's sake.)

Now light travels at the rate of 3 x 10^{10} centimeters per second. There are about $3 \cdot 16$ x 10^8 seconds in a year. A light-year is the distance traversed by light in one year, and is, therefore,

3 x 10^{10} x 3·16 x 10^8 or about 10^{19} centimeters in length.
Our computing machine which is ten billion (10^{10}) light-years
along each edge is, therefore, 10^{29} centimeters long each way
and its volume is 10^{29} x 10^{29} x 10^{29} or 10^{87} cubic centimeters all
told. Since each cubic centimeter can contain 10^{63} neutrinos
the total number of neutrinos that can be packed into a cube a
thousand times the volume of the known universe is 10^{87} x 10^{63}
or 10^{126}.

But these 'neutrinos' are computing units, remember. Let us
suppose that each computing unit is a really super-mechanical
job, capable of testing a billion different amino-acid combinations every second, and let us suppose that each unit keeps
up this mad pace, unrelentingly, for three hundred billion years.

The number of different combinations tested in all that time
would be about 10^{179}.

This number is still approximately zero as compared with
the hemoglobin number. In fact, the chance that the right combination would have been found in all that time would be only
1 in 4 x 10^{440}.

But, you may say, suppose there is more than only one possible hemoglobin combination. It is true, after all, that the
hemoglobin of various species of animals are distinct in their
properties from one another. Well, let's be unfailingly generous.
Let's suppose that every hemoglobin molecule that ever possibly existed on Earth is just a little different from every other.
It would then be only necessary for our giant computing
machine to find any one of 10^{50} possibilities. The chances of
finding any one of those in three hundred billion years with
10^{150} units each turning out a billion answers a second is still
only 1 out of 10^{390}.

It would seem then that if ever a problem were absolutely
incapable of solution, it is the problem of trying to pick out the
exact arrangement of amino-acids in a protein molecule out of
all the different arrangements that are possible.

And yet, in the last few years, biochemists have been making
excellent progress in solving just that sort of problem. The
amino-acid arrangements in the protein, insulin—lack of which
brings on diabetes—was completely worked out in 1953. To be
sure, insulin is only one-fifth the size of hemoglobin, but there

are still just about 3 x 10^{100} possible arrangements of its amino-acids, and that is a most respectable quantity.

How did the biochemists do it?

The fact is that straight trial-and-error technique would have been an unbearable trial and a colossal error. So they used other methods. There *are* other methods, you know.

CHAPTER FOUR

VICTORY ON PAPER

THE key to the answer to the problem of protein structure was found by a Russian. This was Michael Tswett.

In 1906, Tswett submitted a paper to a German botanical journal in which he described a series of experiments involving a new and, as it turned out, revolutionary technique. Tswett was a botanist who was interested in the colored pigments one could soak out of plant leaves by using various solvents. Among those pigments is chlorophyll which plants use to convert solar energy into food and without which life on Earth—except for certain micro-organisms—would quickly become impossible. Naturally, biochemists were yearning at the time to get at those plant pigments, separate one from another and figure out the structure of each. But how was one to go about separating the unholy mess into individual components? Ordinary chemical procedures simply didn't come close to doing the job.

The way Tswett went about it was to dissolve this mess in a liquid called petroleum ether and then pour it through a glass column packed tightly with powdered limestone. The liquid percolated downward and came out at the bottom of the column unchanged and unharmed. The plant pigments which had been dissolved in the liquid, however, remained behind, clinging to the surface of the limestone particles.

Don't think for a moment that the pigment molecules were faced with an easy choice. To be sure they preferred the particle surface, yet the liquid did exert a certain attraction for them. As the liquid passed through the pigment, molecules were slowly and reluctantly dragged down with it, moving downward from limestone particle to limestone particle.

Each individual type of pigment was its own schizophrenic self; each arrived at its own particular compromise in deciding how firmly to remain with the limestone or how willingly accompany the downward-moving liquid. The more tightly they hugged the particles, the more slowly that particular variety of molecule moved downward. The more bibulously they enjoyed their liquid surrounding, the more quickly they moved down.

What was, therefore, originally a disheartening mixture slowly resolved itself into a series of bands of different shades of yellow and green in different places along the column of powdered limestone (*see Figure* 10). If one continued to pour petroleum ether through the column, each band would eventually be washed out through the bottom opening—one at a time. By the time the experiment was completed, the different components of the mixture would be resting contentedly in separate beakers.

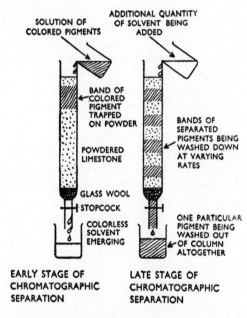

Figure 10. Column chromatography.

Tswett called the technique 'chromatography' from Greek words meaning 'color-writing', though as he pointed out, the principle would work for colorless mixtures as well.

Tswett, unfortunately, was in a poor position. Biochemistry was, at the time, almost the private domain of German scientists and these did not take kindly to the fact that here was a neat, elegant and easy solution to a mystifying and tantalizing problem offered the world by (*a*) a botanist and not a biochemist, and (*b*) a Russian and not a German. Furthermore, in 1910, when Tswett wrote a detailed monograph on chromatography, he wrote in the very best Russian and he might as well have used south-Martian for all the good that did the biochemical world.

On the side of Tswett was only the fact that he was right and that chromatography was destined to become one of the most powerful and widely-used techniques available to the biochemist. The mere fact of his being right, however, was not enough to raise a Russian botanist to a level of equality with a German biochemist, and chromatography dropped dead. (In 1922, an American used chromatography and reported it, but in those days that carried little weight, too.)

Twenty-five years passed from the day of the original discovery. Then, in 1931, German biochemists finally got around to using Tswett's techniques and, what do you know, it worked exactly as he had described.

In the last quarter-century, all sorts of powders have been used to separate individual components out of all sorts of mixtures. Most recently, synthetic substances known as 'ion-exchange resins' have been most useful.

In 1944, came a major refinement. A group of English biochemists abandoned columns and powders and contented themselves with sheets of filter paper (i.e. a kind of porous paper which, in its better grades, is almost pure cellulose).

If one end of a strip or sheet of filter paper is immersed in liquid, the liquid will slowly creep up the filter paper. (You can watch this phenomenon yourself if you have a piece of blotting paper and a bottle of ink handy.) If you keep the filter paper and the liquid in a closed container to prevent evaporation, the liquid will eventually soak through the entire strip if it is not too long.

Now suppose that near the end of a sheet of filter paper you were to place a drop or two of a solution containing a mixture of similar substances and then let the drop dry. Next, dip that end of the sheet into a liquid, being careful to keep the dried drop of mixture above the level of the liquid, and enclose the whole system to cut down evaporation.

Up creeps the liquid. In a short while it reaches and passes the dried drop of mixed substances. Each different component of that mixture is now faced with the usual schizophrenic dilemma. Shall it stay put or shall it let go? Shall it ignore the liquid or shall it go along with it? Each substance makes the usual individual compromise. Each substance moves along with the liquid in a laggard and hesitant way. (Referring back to a home experiment with a blotter and a drop of ink, note that the pigment particles in the ink do not travel as far along the blotting paper as does the water content of the ink, so that the blue drop of spread-out ink is encircled by a colorless damp spot.)

As you can guess, each component of the mixture travels at its own rate. By the time the liquid has soaked a foot or two along the paper, the original spot has become a whole series of spots.

Theoretically, each spot of the series should now contain a single separate substance. Actually, however, in any mixture containing a number of similar substances, it often happens that two or three may have such similar rates of travel that at the end, they remain in a single spot.

For that reason, the paper is dried, turned on its side, and immersed in a different type of liquid altogether. The first liquid, for instance, might have been a mixture of butyl alcohol and water; the second, a mixture of phenol and water. Substances which have similar rates of travel in one liquid are very likely to have different rates of travel in a second liquid. The two or three substances which had previously stuck together buddy-fashion, bid one another a fond adieu and separate. The whole process is diagrammed (*Figure* 11).

This technique is called two-dimensional paper chromatography. Its advantage over the earlier column chromatography is that the equipment needed is dirt-cheap and that very small quantities of material can be handled without difficulty.

Once the spots are separated; once each substance occupies its own individual place on the paper; there is the problem of

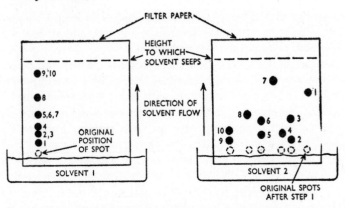

Figure II. Two-dimensional paper chromatography.

finding them. Usually, the substances being separated are colorless and the filter paper, after drying has a disconcertingly virginal emptiness about it.

The problem can be solved handily, however. For instance, under ultraviolet light, the spots may fluoresce or appear black. In either case, pencil lines can be drawn about them. Or else, two sheets are prepared in identical fashion and one is treated with some chemical which will combine with some or all of the substances to form a visible color. The spots stand out neatly; the colored sheet is superimposed on the untouched sheet, and you take it from there.

Once the spots are located, they can be cut out. Each substance can be dissolved individually out of the paper. Each can be identified and manipulated further. Peace, it's wonderful.

And why am I talking about this? Where are all these filter paper manipulations getting me?

Well, it is paper chromatography which enabled chemists to solve the problem which in the previous chapter I went to great lengths to demonstrate to be 'impossible' of solution. That problem involves the structure of protein molecules.

Each protein molecule is made up of hundreds or even thousands of simpler substances called amino-acids—of some twenty different varieties—which are strung together like pearls in a necklace. The number of different ways in which a particular combination of amino-acids can be arranged even for a protein of only average size is so great that all of space and time —literally, not poetically, speaking—is insufficient to allow each possible way to be tested in order that the one arrangement which actually makes up that protein be discovered.

Nor is this 'impossible' problem just a matter of idle curiosity on the part of long-haired biochemists who have nothing better to do.

In case you wonder about that, let's bring insulin to the front of the stage.

Insulin is a protein molecule which is manufactured by certain specialized cells of the pancreas (a gland located just under the stomach). As it is formed, it is secreted into the blood in amounts adjusted to the needs of the body at the moment. The blood carries it to all the cells of the body and there it somehow supervises the utilization of sugars and fats for energy-production purposes.

Exactly how insulin does this is a matter of considerable dispute. Some biochemists think it acts as a control on one particular chemical reaction, through which the entire series of reactions is hastened or slowed according to need. Other biochemists think insulin coats the surface of each cell and controls the flow of raw materials entering, adjusting the cell chemistry in that fashion.

Whatever the exact mechanism, insulin is vital. Every once in a while, the pancreas stops manufacturing this key protein in some individual. The chemistry of the body promptly goes wrong. Glucose—a kind of sugar used by the body for quick energy production—is processed inefficiently. It accumulates in the blood and spills over into the urine. Sugar in the urine or, better still, too much sugar in the blood, is an almost certain sign of the disease called diabetes.

Because a diabetic utilizes his food inefficiently, he grows hungrier; yet though he may increase his food intake, he will lose weight nevertheless. He needs extra water to carry off the sugar continually passing through his kidneys, so he must drink more and urinate more. The disease has its ramifications. The diabetic is more prone to various infections than is the normal person, he is much more likely to suffer from hardening of the arteries if the disease is allowed to take its course.

Although diabetes tends to run in families, its onset in an individual is unpredictable and unpreventable. Once it comes, it is incurable. (Careful diet may delay its approach and keep its effects relatively mild.) Diabetes is the most common chemical disorder of the human body. Millions suffer from this serious disease.

Fortunately, in the 1920s, some Canadian scientists—who later got the Nobel Prize for it—discovered how to isolate insulin from the pancreases of cattle. Using such insulin as a replacement for that which their own pancreases can no longer supply, human diabetics can now live reasonably normal lives.

The use of insulin as a treatment (*not* cure) for diabetes has certain difficulties about it. First, it's only source is the pancreas of slaughtered cattle, swine and so on, and each animal has but one pancreas. There is, therefore, an upper limit to how much insulin can be made available. Secondly, insulin cannot be taken by mouth, since it is digested and made useless in the stomach and intestines. It must be injected by hypodermic needle, which is troublesome.

Now *if* the exact structure of insulin were known—not just the approximate structure but the *exact* structure—biochemists might be better able to decide from that structure its method of working, now under such dispute. They might make an intelligent guess at what features of its molecule were most necessary for its purpose and synthesize a simpler molecule containing those features. If the simpler molecules worked to control diabetes, it would mean that there would be a potentially limitless supply of drug not dependent on cattle. Furthermore, it might be simple enough to withstand digestion, in which case it might be taken by mouth.

This sort of procedure has actually been carried out in the case of certain alkaloids. The structure of the local anesthetic cocaine, was worked out and simpler substances, containing the essential features of the molecule, were synthesized. Such a synthetic substitute-cocaine is Novocaine which, in some respects, is more useful than the natural drug.

So you see then that in the case of insulin, at least, the exact arrangement of the amino-acids is anything but an academic problem. It has an important application to a serious health problem.

The size of the insulin molecule can be determined in a number of ways and it is found to have a molecular weight of 12,000. This is 660 times as great as the weight of a water molecule but only one-fifth the weight of an averagely-sized protein such as hemoglobin. Despite its small size for a protein, insulin still has room for about a hundred amino-acid components, which makes the problem of its exact structure a sizable one.

The insulin molecule can be broken up into the individual amino-acid components by prolonged treatment with acid. Before 1944 this wouldn't have helped much because many of the amino-acids are quite similar in structure and it is the devil's own job to tackle the analysis of amino-acid mixtures in the expectation of determining how much of each amino-acid is present. With paper chromatography, however, the problem is simple. A drop of the mixture is placed on the filter paper, two different solvents are used in two different directions, and the various amino-acids are spread out neatly so that the identity of each and the quantity present can be determined.

In this way, it was found that the molecule of insulin contained 96 amino-acids of 18 different types. For our purposes, the names of the different amino-acids are unnecessary. We can list them in alphabetical order and call them A, B, C, through R.

The fifth amino-acid—in alphabetical order—is different from the rest in that it is a double molecule, or a two-headed molecule if you prefer. One end of it can form part of one amino-acid chain and the other end of it can form part of a second amino-acid chain. For that reason, it will be referred to as E-E, instead of simply E.

Table XIII lists the different amino-acids and gives the number of each which is found in the insulin molecule. The number of ways in which those ninety-six amino-acids can be arranged in a chain to form a protein molecule is three googols; that is, 3×10^{100} or a 3 followed by 100 zeros. I won't go through the gyrations I went through in a previous chapter to prove that this is a large number. Take my word for it. The total number of all subatomic particles contained in a trillion suns is nothing in comparison to it.

Which of the three googols of possible arrangements is the right one? Give up? Well, a group of British biochemists under

TABLE XIII

Amino-Acid Composition of Insulin	
Type of Amino-Acid	*Number in Insulin Molecule*
A	6
B	2
C	4
D	2
E-E	6
F	8
G	2
H	12
I	4
J	2
K	12
L	2
M	6
N	2
O	6
P	2
Q	8
R	10
Total	96

the direction of Dr. F. Sanger didn't. They began working on the problem in 1945 or thereabouts.

One point of attack in any amino-acid chain are the end amino-acids. Suppose you had the chain, F-G-H-I-J-K. Obviously, F and K differ from the other amino-acids in that each has one end free. F has its acid side free and K has its amino side free. (Arbitrarily, I write the chain so that the acid ends of each amino-acid component is at the left and the amino ends of each at the right. It could be done the other way around just as easily.)

Sanger and his groups discovered that if an amino-acid chain is treated with a certain colored chemical—which is now called Sanger's Reagent after him—it will attach itself to the unattached amino group at the extreme right-hand end of the chain. You would have this situation in the case we have presented: F-G-H-I-J-KS, where S represents Sanger's Reagent.

If, after treatment, the chain is broken into individual amino-acids by acid treatment, Sanger's Reagent remains combined and you're left with F, G, H, I, J, and KS. The mixture can be chromatographed and the KS is extremely easy to locate since, like Sanger's Reagent alone, it is colored and the other amino-acids are not. The KS can be dissolved out of the paper, Sanger's Reagent can be forced off and the amino-acid identified. In this way, one can decide the particular amino-acid which exists at the extreme right end of an amino-acid chain.

Sanger's group applied this principle to insulin and found that every molecule of insulin yielded *four* amino-acids to which Sanger's reagent was attached. Two of these amino-acids were H and two were M (using our alphabetical arrangement).

The only conclusion was that every insulin molecule consists of four separate amino-acid chains held together by the double-headed amino-acid E-E of which there are six in every molecule. The picture so far is shown diagrammatically in (*Figure* 12).

Now there is a way of breaking the double-headed E-E into two single-headed fragments, E and E, without disturbing other portions of the amino-acid chains. The chemical used is one called performic acid.

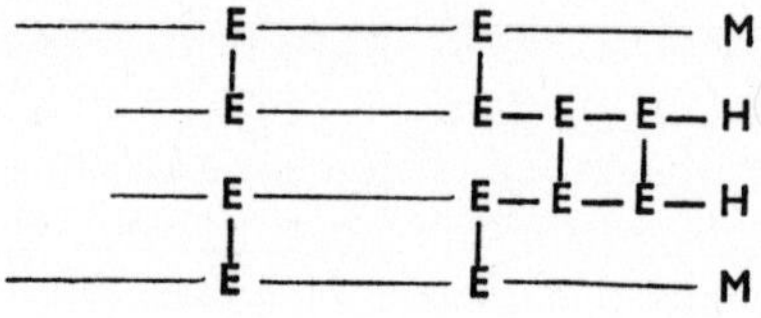

Figure 12. Diagrammatic Structure of Insulin Molecule.

Sanger and company treated insulin with performic acid—what an opportunity for puns—and found themselves left with the four isolated amino-acid chains shown in (*Figure* 13).

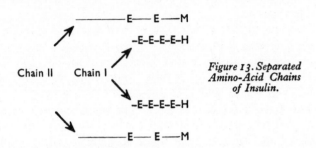

Figure 13. Separated Amino-Acid Chains of Insulin.

The two chains ending in H and containing four E's apiece turned out to be identical, judging from the results of various tests. Let's refer to such a chain as Chain I. The two chains ending in M and containing two E's apiece are also identical. Call such a chain Chain II. Since Chain I and Chain II are different in structure, they have different chemical properties and can be separated easily enough.

Once separated, Chain I and Chain II can be separately broken up into individual amino-acids by treatment with acid. The resulting amino-acid soup from each type of chain can be and was analyzed by paper chromatography. In this way, the different amino-acids in each chain can be identified both as to nature and quantity. The results are shown in (Table XIV).

Notice that Chain I consists of twenty-one amino-acids and Chain II of thirty amino-acids. Since each insulin molecule consists of two of Chain I and two of Chain II, the total number of amino-acids in insulin comes to one hundred and two. Earlier, I said ninety-six. This is no discrepancy, however, since in breaking apart the four amino-acid chains of insulin, the six E-E amino-acids were converted to twelve E amino-acids, thus adding six amino-acids to the total, 96 plus 6 equals 102, Q. E. D.

Have we achieved anything? Well, now it is only necessary to determine the arrangement of the amino-acids in each of the two varieties of chains. The number of possible arrangements

TABLE XIV

Amino-Acid Composition of Chain I and Chain II		
Type of Amino-Acid	*Number in Chain I*	*Number in Chain II*
A	1	2
B	0	1
C	2	0
D	0	1
E	4	2
F	2	2
G	0	1
H	3	3
I	0	2
J	1	0
K	2	4
L	0	1
M	0	3
N	0	1
O	2	1
P	0	1
Q	2	2
R	2	3
Totals	21	30

in Chain II is 3×10^{27} and that of Chain I is 6×10^{15}. These aren't exactly small numbers, but in comparison to 10^{100}, they are nothing. Nothing at all. Why 3×10^{27} is only half the size of the number of grams of mass contained in the Earth. As for 6×10^{15}, it is only six million billion, which is laughable.

So Sanger and company have made progress.

Where next?

Suppose we take Chain II and subject it to acid treatment. The acid breaks the links between the amino-acids more or less at random, sometimes here, sometimes there, in no particular order. If you let it work to the bitter end, all the links between amino-acids are broken. But what if you stop the action by neutralizing the acid before the job is completed? In that case, you end up with various fragments of the chain that haven't been completely broken apart. Two amino-acids remain stuck together from one portion of the chain, two from another, three from still another, four from yet another. In short, you get a potpourri of just about every possible combination of two, three, or four amino-acids that the chain can yield.

This potpourri can be partially separated. Actually, five different groups of chain fragments can be isolated by conventional chemical treatment. Each group is still a complex mixture, of course, yet each group can be separated easily enough into its different components by two-dimensional paper chromatography.

Once separated, each individual chain fragment can be dissolved out of the paper and placed in a separate test tube. Each fragment can be separately treated with acid and this time the acid is allowed to do the complete job. Each chain fragment is cut up into individual amino-acids and *that* mixture then takes the filter-paper path to analysis. The individual amino-acids in each separate chain are thus identified.

In this way, it is found that one chain fragment consists of amino-acids E, H, and R. Another one consists of D, G, R, and M. And so on and so on and so on.

But what about the order of amino-acids in these fragments? If a fragment contains E, H, and R, is its structure E-H-R, E-R-H, R-E-H, R-H-E, H-E-R, or H-R-E?

One piece of information can be obtained by treating a particular chain fragment with Sanger's Reagent before subjecting it to acid and thus identifying the amino-acid at the right-hand end of the fragment.

If the fragment happens to consist only of two amino-acids, that gives us its structure at once. If it contains A and B and it is B that is on the right, obviously its structure is A-B. Nothing else is possible. In this way, nearly thirty-two amino-acid fragments were identified as coming from the partial break-up of Chain II.

From that point, a process of reasoning follows that is

similar to the type used in solving jigsaw puzzles or crypto-grams.

For instance, Chain II contains only one of amino-acid, D. Two different chains of two amino-acids, each containing D, were isolated. One had the structure G-D and the other D-R. Obviously then, Chain II must contain the combination G-D-R. It is the only combination from which one can obtain both G-D and D-R.

There is an amino-acid chain of three amino-acids which contains D, R and M, with M at the right-hand end. The chain of three can only be D-R-M or R-D-M. But we know that R follows the only D in the chain. The three combination can only be D-R-M. Furthermore, we know that G precedes the only D in Chain II. So, it is now known that Chain II contains the following sequence of four amino-acids, G-D-R-M.

Analysis proceeds in this manner. There is only one amino-acid, B, in the chain. Since H-B and B-F are found, the sequence H-B-F is established.

Again there is only one amino-acid N present. A fragment of structure N-P is found. Also one containing three amino-acids with N at the right end is found. The latter is either L-A-N or A-L-N. No fragment of structure L-A is ever found, however. One of structure A-L *is* found. The three-amino-acid chain must, therefore, be A-L-N and since there is also the N-P previously mentioned, a four-amino-acid sequence, A-L-N-P, has been established.

Little by little the chain sequence is put together until finally the only (!!!!) arrangement of thirty amino-acids which will account for *all* the chain fragments located by paper chromatography is decided upon. One arrangement out of 3×10^{27} possibilities. One arrangement only. It's like looking for a particular two-gram chunk of matter—1/14th of an ounce— somewhere in Earth's massive rotundity, *and finding it*.

By similar methods, the arrangement of amino-acids in Chain I is also determined. The arrangements for both chains is shown in (*Figure* 14). The manner in which two Chain I's and two Chain II's are hooked up to form insulin becomes a mere detail, and it can be stated that Sanger and his group have determined the exact amino-acid structure of insulin.

C-E-Q-C-H-K-H-Q-K-O-E-R-O-A-E-E-F-F-R-J-H
Chain I

A-L-N-P-Q-M-M-H-B-F-H-E-R-K-Q-K-A-F-R-K-I-O-H-E-K-I-G-D-R-M
Chain II

Figure 14. Amino-acid arrangement in Chain I and Chain II.

It would be pleasant if I could proceed now to say that the determination of insulin's structure shed an immediate and brilliant light on insulin's method of working or that it served to present an immediate hope for an improved treatment of diabetes.

Unfortunately, I can't. So far, the victory on (filter) paper remains only a victory on paper as far as clinicians are concerned.

The arrangement of amino-acids in insulin seems to have no significance. We stare at it and it makes no illuminating sense. Minor changes in the insulin molecule destroy its effectiveness completely and no one part of the molecule appears more important than another part.

Is no further progress possible? Can no chemical even slightly simpler than insulin possibly substitute for it?

I don't know. Yet I'm not entirely depressed, either.

It took Sanger and his men eight years to solve the 'impossible' problem of finding one arrangement out of several googols of possible arrangements. We shouldn't object to giving biochemists a few more years to see what other impossibilities they can knock off.

CHAPTER FIVE

THE ABNORMALITY OF BEING NORMAL

A COMMON catch-phrase is the one that goes, 'There is no such thing as a normal person.'

The question, though, is this: '*Why* is there no such thing as a normal person?'

We'll get to that.

People sometimes say, with a certain smugness: 'A normal person is like a perfect gas or absolute zero; a useful abstraction that doesn't exist in actual reality.'

This has the virtue of placing psychology on a kind of par with the physical sciences, but doesn't help explain *why* a normal person doesn't exist in actual reality.

We know why a perfect gas doesn't exist. A perfect gas is one in which the individual molecules are assumed to occupy mathematical points and to have zero volume. It is also one in which the attraction of neighbouring molecules for one another is zero. When these criteria are met, the way a gas behaves can be readily calculated from a few basic assumptions, some geometry and a bit of statistical technique. In this way, certain neat and orderly 'gas laws' are evolved.

Unfortunately, however, the molecules of all actual gases invariably take up a certain volume. Small as they are, they are never mathematical points. Moreover, molecules always have some attraction for one another. Sometimes the attraction is minute, but it is never zero.

Both facts invalidate the gas laws. In order to account for the behavior of actual gases, physical chemists have learned to make empirical allowance for the manner in which actual molecules fall short of the 'ideal'.

Any actual gas can be made to behave so as to approach an ideal gas. If a gas is placed under very low pressure, its molecules move apart. As they move apart, their attraction for one another decreases. The volume of the individual molecule, moreover, becomes so small compared to the space between molecules, that the individual molecule can be considered more and more as a simple point. In this way, the conditions of the perfect gas are approached. (The same is true if the temperature of a gas is raised.)

An actual gas becomes a perfect gas at zero pressure. Unfortunately, at zero pressure the molecules are at infinite distance from one another and we have no gas at all, only the very best vacuum.

A perfect gas is therefore a 'limiting condition'. It can never be actually reached. It can be approached asymptotically (fancy word for: you-can-get-closer-and-closer-and-closer-but-you-can't-ever-quite-reach-it) but only asymptotically.

Now for absolute zero.

Absolute zero is the temperature at which all molecular motion ceases. In actual practice, it is impossible to reach that temperature. Temperatures as low as a few thousandths of a degree above absolute zero have been reached but that is no sign that the goal is within sight. It is hard to get from 4 degrees above absolute zero to 2 degrees above. It is just as hard to travel from 2 to 1; equally as hard to go from 1 to 0·5; again as hard to go from 0·5 to 0·25 and so on.

Again, we have a limiting condition that can be approached only asymptotically.

Now we get back to our 'normal' person. If the normal person were like a perfect gas or absolute zero, it too might represent a limiting condition of some sort, a limit which could be approached but not reached.

We can easily imagine one sort of limit of human behavior. We can think of a human being who is incredibly strong, incredibly wise, incredibly virtuous, incredibly all-that-is-praiseworthy, a superman, a godlike creature. But this is no 'normal person'; this is more like an 'ideal person' and we can see quite plainly that a man so incredibly this and that is also incredibly scarce.

You can see that the adjectives used for these limiting abstractions are very suggestive: 'perfect', 'absolute', 'ideal'. Adjectives such as that *fit* unreachable limits.

But how then does the word 'normal' come to be applied to

something which seems to be an abstraction? The word 'normal' is synonymized in the dictionary by such words as 'common', 'natural', 'ordinary', 'regular', 'typical', and 'usual'. When we say that a normal person doesn't exist, aren't we indulging in a contradiction in terms? How can something which is common, natural, ordinary, regular, typical and usual not exist?

Well, then, what is a normal person to a psychologist? He is the sum of the million and one (or is it trillion and one?) individual characteristics that go into the making of a human being. And in every one of these characteristics, he is normal. That is, in the case of every component characteristic, our normal human being has whatever attribute is common, natural, ordinary, regular, typical and usual.

Some of the characteristics are universal. Every living human being breathes, everyone has a heart that beats and so on. In these respects, every living human being is normal.

There are also factors that are not universal. For instance, a person may have an overwhelming urge to kill strangers who have done him no harm. On the other hand, he may not have. The second alternative is normal in the sense that it is common, natural, etc., but it is not universal. There *are* a certain number of people who have uncontrollable homicidal drives. To have such a drive is an abnormal characteristic; to not have it is normal. Our 'normal person' would therefore not have one.

In any given individual, any factor in his makeup can be considered either normal or abnormal. The normal is that which occurs in most people; perhaps in nearly all; in some cases, actually in all. (Mind you, the normal characteristic need not be a particularly admirable one, merely a common one. All people are selfish, to an extent; cowardly, to an extent; stubborn, to an extent; stupid, to an extent. Our 'normal man' would be selfish, cowardly, stubborn and stupid to the normal extent.)

Now, then, if most people are normal in any given characteristic, why are there no 'normal people' who are normal in all characteristics?

In other words, if we add common, natural, ordinary, regular, typical and usual characteristics together, why don't we end up with common, natural, ordinary, regular, typical and usual people?

Let's switch, temporarily, from people to atoms, and see if we can find the answer?

The atoms of most elements consist of two or more different varieties that are similar in chemical properties but different in certain other respects. These varieties are referred to as isotopes of that element.

Some elements are split up fairly evenly among two or more isotopes. Some, on the other hand, are preponderantly (but often not entirely) one isotope, with other isotopes occurring only rarely. Now it so happens that of the elements that make up the body, the most important ones fall into the second classification.

At this point, please look at Table XV.

By 'fractional occurrence', I mean, of course, the fraction of the atoms of a certain element (in any random sample) which are a particular isotope. For instance, if we concentrate on hydrogen, then what the table is saying is that out of every 100,000 hydrogen atoms, 99,984 (on the average) are hydrogen–1 and only 16 are hydrogen–2. (Never mind the significance of

TABLE XV

Element	Major Isotopes		Minor Isotopes	
	Name	Fractional Occurrence	Name	Fractional Occurrence
Hydrogen	Hydrogen–1	0·99984	Hydrogen–2	0·00016
Carbon	Carbon–12	0·9888	Carbon–13	0·0112
Nitrogen	Nitrogen–14	0·9962	Nitrogen–15	0·0038
Oxygen	Oxygen–16	0·9976	Oxygen–17 ⎱ Oxygen–18 ⎰	0·0024
Sulfur	Sulfur–32	0·9506	Sulfur–33 ⎱ Sulfur–34 ⎰	0·0494
Iron	Iron–56	0·9157	Iron–54 ⎱ Iron–57 ⎰ Iron–58 ⎰	0·0843

the numbers that are used to distinguish isotopes from one another. That's not important for our purpose here.)

Put it another way. Suppose you are sitting before a sack of hydrogen atoms which have been expanded to the size of marbles and suppose you are dipping in blindly and taking out any hydrogen atom you touched. The chances are 99,984 out of 100,000 that you would pull out a hydrogen-1 atom. The chances are only 16 out of 100,000 that you would pull out a hydrogen-2 atom.

Under those conditions you would naturally expect to pull out a hydrogen-1 atom at any particular try. If you did pull one out, you would consider the event a 'normal' one. Every once in a while, though, you would withdraw your hand and find yourself staring at a hydrogen-2 atom and you could not help but be astonished. It would be an 'abnormal' occurrence.

The same would be true for the other elements listed in the table, though not to the same extent as hydrogen. The other elements are not quite so preponderantly one isotope as is hydrogen. Still, even iron is more than 9/10 one isotope and less than 1/10 the other three put together.

Therefore, let's call hydrogen-1, carbon-12, nitrogen-14, oxygen-16, sulfur-32 and iron-56 the 'normal' isotopes. The others are 'abnormal' isotopes. (Naturally, I'm not implying there is anything morally wrong with hydrogen-2, carbon-13 or any of the others, or anything physically distorted, either. I am simply calling that isotope normal which is the common, natural, ordinary, etc. one.)

Now let's proceed. Hydrogen atoms don't exist by themselves under ordinary conditions. They tie up in pairs to form hydrogen molecules. You can see, then, that three different kinds of combinations of two hydrogen atoms (three different kinds of molecules, that is) can be formed if the combination is formed in a random manner. A hydrogen-1 can tie up with a hydrogen-1. A hydrogen-1 can tie up with a hydrogen-2. A hydrogen-2 can tie up with a hydrogen-2.

Naturally, most of the combinations are hydrogen-1 with hydrogen-1, simply because there are so few hydrogen-2 atoms present. But exactly what proportion of the hydrogen molecules would be hydrogen-1, hydrogen-1 combinations.

The probability of any given hydrogen atom being hydrogen-1 is the same as its fractional occurrence, *i.e.* 0·99984. The probability of a second hydrogen atom being hydrogen-1 is also 0·99984. Now what's the chance of picking out two hydrogen atoms from that sack of ours and finding them *both* hydrogen-1?

The probability of two occurrences *both* happening is determined by multiplying the probabilities of each occurrence happening individually.

In other words the probability of any two hydrogen atoms *both* being hydrogen-1 (as in a hydrogen-1, hydrogen-1 molecule) is 0·99984 multiplied by 0·99984. The answer to that is 0·99968. That means that 99,968 hydrogen molecules out of every 100,000 are hydrogen-1, hydrogen-1 combinations. Only 32 out of every 100,000 are hydrogen-1, hydrogen-2 or hydrogen-2, hydrogen-2 combinations.

The hydrogen-1, hydrogen-1 molecules are 'normal' in the sense that they are the common, natural, ordinary, regular, typical and usual ones. The other types of molecules are abnormal.

We can stop at this point and make a trial definition which may turn out to be a good one or may not. Let's say this: Any molecule is normal if it is made up entirely of normal isotopes. (Notice that this is analogous to saying that a 'normal person' is one who is made up entirely of normal individual characteristics).

Now to proceed. Note that the fractional occurrence of normal hydrogen molecules, 0·99968, is not quite as high as the fractional occurrence of normal hydrogen atoms, 0·99984. This makes sense since a number of the normal hydrogen-1 isotopes are 'spoiled' by hooking up with hydrogen-2 isotopes to form part of the abnormal hydrogen-1, hydrogen-2 molecules.

We can also consider this from the standpoint of simple arithmetic. Whenever two numbers less than 1 are multiplied, the product is smaller than either of the original numbers. The closer the numbers are to 1, the less the shrinkage of the product.

If the numbers were actually 1, then there would be no shrinkage. The product would be 1, too. If the probability of the occurrence of hydrogen–1 were 1, that would mean that every hydrogen atom would be hydrogen–1, without exception. They would all be normal. In that case, every hydrogen molecule would be the normal hydrogen–1, hydrogen–1 combination since there would be no other kind of hydrogen to interfere. This is analogous to people being made up of universal traits only, such as all having pumping lungs and beating hearts.

(In probability problems, all numbers are 1 or less than 1. Since 1 represents universality or certainty, a probability greater than 1 can not be spoken of. What is more probable than the universal or certain?)

Observe another thing about the multiplication of numbers less than 1. If you keep on multiplying them, the products keep on getting smaller. Suppose you multiplied 0·99984 by itself ten times. The answer would be 0·99816. That's the arithmetical way of saying that if you pulled ten hydrogen atoms at a time out of your sack, the chances that all of them would be hydrogen–1 without exception is 99,816 out of 100,000. The chance of finding at least one hydrogen–2 atom in that group of ten is 184 out of 100,000.

Hydrogen molecules are very simple. They contain only two atoms apiece. What if we took a more complicated molecule, such as ethyl alcohol? The molecule of ethyl alcohol is made up of two carbon atoms, six hydrogen atoms, and one oxygen atom.

To find the frequency with which normal molecules of ethyl alcohol (those containing only normal isotopes) occur, we must multiply the fractional occurrence of carbon–12 by itelf (two carbon atoms, you see), multiply that product by the fractional occurrence of hydrogen–1 six times (six hydrogen atoms) and multiply that by the fractional occurrence of oxygen–16 (one oxygen atom).

The arithmetic would go like this: 0·9888 x 0·9888 x 0·99984 x 0·99984 x 0·99984 x 0·99984 x 0·99984 x 0·99984 x 0·9976 = 0·97432. Out of every 100,000 ethyl alcohol molecules, 97,432 are normal and 2,568 are abnormal.

That's a larger number of abnormal molecules than you expected perhaps, but let's go on. Ethyl alcohol is still a small molecule. What if we take a molecule of table sugar which is made up of twelve carbons, twenty-two hydrogens, and eleven oxygens. We have to multiply 45 numbers together and once that is done, we find the probability of a normal molecule of table sugar to be 0·84748. Out of every 100,000 molecules of table sugar, 84,748 are normal and 15,252 molecules are abnormal.

The normals still have it by a considerable majority, but it is nothing like the preponderance in the case of the smaller molecules. Interesting!

What about larger molecules still? A typical fat molecule contains 57 carbon atoms, 104 hydrogen atoms and 6 oxygen atoms. Multiplying all the appropriate probabilities the appropriate number of times, we come up with a final value of 0·50901.

The truth is, then, that just about half the fat molecules are normal, by the definition of normality we are using. The other half are abnormal.

Now let's pass on to the hemoglobin molecule, the red substance in the blood which absorbs oxygen in the lungs and carries it to the tissues. Its molecule is made up of 2,778 carbon atoms, 5,303 hydrogen atoms, 1,308 oxygen atoms, 749 nitrogen atoms, 9 sulfur atoms and 4 iron atoms. Now, we must *really* multiply and it is at such times that I am most grateful for the existence of logarithms and calculating machines.

The answer to all these calculations is something smaller, as you ought to expect, than anything we've had so far. It is, in fact, 0·0000000000000001134. This means that about one hemoglobin molecule out of every ten million billion is 'normal'.

And let's see what *that* means. In a single drop of blood, there are about 250,000,000 red blood corpuscles. In one single drop of blood, that is. Well, now, if six hundred men pool all their 'normal' hemoglobin molecules, they will have enough to fill exactly one (I repeat, *one*) of those corpuscles. That single corpuscle will contain hemoglobin completely free of abnormal isotopes. Every other red blood corpuscle in every drop of blood of all six hundred men will contain only hemoglobin molecules with one or more abnormal isotopes included.

You see, then, that if we insist on considering a hemoglobin molecule to be normal only when it contains normal isotopes and nothing else, we are going to end up with a 'normal' molecule that is neither common, natural, ordinary, regular, typical nor usual. Anything but, in fact.

What we have called a 'normal' molecule turns out, as you can now see, to be indeed a limiting case, one which *can* be reached but is not very likely to be except *very* rarely. A hemoglobin molecule can be made up of all normal atoms or, alternatively, of all abnormal atoms. Each is a limiting case. Or else, it can be made up of any combination of normal and abnormal atoms. Those are the in-between cases.

If the limiting case is so rare (the one where all the atoms are abnormal is many-and-many times rarer than the one we have just considered), are any of the in-between cases more common. If so, which is most common, and how do we find out?

Let's simplify once again and take up a case where there are only two alternatives, each of exactly equal occurrence. The most convenient example involves coin-tossing. Here we have heads and tails, one of each, and we can play with those exclusively.

If you throw a coin once (an honest coin, of course), your chance of throwing heads is 0·5 and your chance of throwing tails is 0·5. Fifty-fifty, in other words.

If you throw a coin twice, you may get two heads (one limiting case) or two tails (the other limiting case) or one head and one tail (the in-between case). The chance of getting two heads is 0·5 x 0·5 or 0·25. The chance of getting two tails is 0·5 x 0·5 or 0·25.

So far, so good. However, the chance of getting one head and one tail is 0·5, twice as good as getting two heads or two tails.

You may wonder why that is so. After all the chance of throwing a head is 0·5 and the chance of throwing a tail is 0·5 and multiplying them together leaves a 0·25 chance of throwing both. Ah, but you may throw the head-tail combination in either of two ways. You may throw the head first and then the tail, or the tail first, then the head. That gives you 0·25 x 2 or 0·5, as said. Two heads or two tails can only be thrown one way.

The rule is that the probability of limiting cases (all heads or all tails) is obtained by multiplying the probability of one head or one tail by the number of tosses.

For the in-between cases, the probability obtained in this way must be further multiplied by the number of different ways (always greater than one) in which the particular in-between case can occur.

Thus, if you threw the coin eight times, the possible combinations would have the following probabilities:

eight heads	0·0039 × 1 way	0·0039
seven heads, one tail	0·0039 × 8 ways	0·0312
six heads, two tails	0·0039 × 28 ways	0·1092
five heads, three tails	0·0039 × 56 ways	0·2184
four heads, four tails	0·0039 × 70 ways	0·2730
three heads, five tails	0·0039 × 56 ways	0·2184
two heads, six tails	0·0039 × 28 ways	0·1092
one head, seven tails	0·0039 × 8 ways	0·0312
eight tails	0·0039 × 1 way	0·0039

(These probabilities should add up to exactly 1. They don't. They add up to 0·9984 due to the fact that I have rounded off the decimal points, and let the error accumulate. As for the number of ways in which each combination can occur, they can be determined very easily by binomial theorem, which sounds impressive, but isn't very difficult really—or, I assure you faithfully, I wouldn't be able to do it.)

The most frequent combination occurring in eight throws is that of four heads and four tails. To be sure, even that would turn up only a little oftener than a quarter of the time so that it couldn't really be said to be normal. Certainly, though, it is the least abnormal of the combinations.

Now notice that the most common case is the one in which heads and tails are represented according to their comparative probabilities. The probability of throwing a head is 0·5 and that of throwing a tail is 0·5. Therefore in the set of eight throws, the most common combination is the one where 0·5 of the throws are heads and 0·5 are tails (four of each).

Without going through any figuring at all, I'd know that the most common combination occurring in a hundred successive throws would be 50 heads and 50 tails. It would be less common (0·1115) than the most common case in the eight-throw problem, occurring only one-tenth of the time. As the number of throws increases, the number of possible combinations increases and the probabilities have to be spread continuously thinner to cover more and more combinations. Still, the fifty-fifty combination would be commoner than anything else.

Furthermore, if for some reason the probability of throwing a head was 0·9 and that of throwing a tail was 0·1, then we can say confidently, without figuring, that in a total of a hundred throws the most common combination would be 90 heads and 10 tails.

The situation may not always be as conveniently even as that. Suppose that the probabilities are 0·9 for heads and 0·1 for tails and you are interested in sets of 68 throws. Then you pick the whole number ratio that is nearest to the proportion of 0·9 to 0·1. In this case, your most frequently occurring combination would be 61 heads and 7 tails.

Or suppose you tossed the coin twice. Your most frequently occurring combination would be 2 heads and no tails. (That's closer to 0·9/0·1 than the next possible combination, 1 head and 1 tail, would be.)

I'm going through all this for a specific reason. I'm going to determine the most frequently occurring combination in hemoglobin and I don't want to have to use the binomial theorem with four-figure numbers. Logarithms, computing machines and all, it would still be tedious.

But first, I must make one more point. You may have noticed that when two alternatives are of equal probability, as in coin-tossing, the in-between cases (heads and tails mixed) are always more probable than the limiting cases (all heads or all tails).

When one alternative is more probable than the other, however, sets made up of a small number of individual items will show one limiting case (that composed only of the more probable alternative) to be the most probable combination. We mentioned several such. For instance, ten hydrogen atoms drawn at random are all hydrogen–1 (a limiting case) 99,816 times out of 100,000.

As the number of individual items making up a set increases, however, the in-between cases gradually become more common than the limiting cases, however lopsided the two alternatives are. Hemoglobin, made up of more than 10,000 atoms, has reached this stage even though the probability of the occurrence of the normal isotopes (one alternative) is way and ahead of the probability of the occurrence of the abnormal isotopes (the other alternative).

For instance, hemoglobin has 2,778 carbon atoms. The frequency of carbon–12 is 0·9888 and that of carbon–13 is 0·0112. Dividing the 2,778 carbon atoms in that ratio, we find that the most frequently occurring hemoglobin molecule is one with 2,747 carbon–12 atoms and 31 carbon–13 atoms. Using the same system for the other atoms, we find that the most frequently occurring hemoglobin molecule has also 3 oxygen–18 atoms, 1 hydrogen–2 atom and 1 nitrogen–15 atom. This makes for a total of 36 abnormal isotopes in the most frequently occurring hemoglobin molecule.

Even this most frequently occurring combination occurs very infrequently. There are something like a hundred trillion possible combinations, so considerable room has to be left for most of the others. (Not for all, though. Some are so rare that they aren't likely to occur even once anywhere on earth.)

In going back to human beings, now, we have little need to dwell on any points. Normal plus normal plus normal-ever-so-many-times does *not* equal normal. It equals highly abnormal, and it is a limiting case.

The number of individual factors—physical, mental, temperamental and emotional—making up a human being are so high that no combination can possibly be called normal in the dictionary meaning of the term. All combinations are tremendously abnormal, and if some combinations are a trifle less abnormal than others, the one the psychologists picked, *their* 'normal man', is definitely not among them.

In fact, any statistical abstraction involving something as complex as the human being is suspect. However handy such may be in computing actuarial tables and predicting elections, it can give rise to great and unnecessary grief through misconstruction by ordinary people in the ordinary business of life.

Still, as long as psychologists use the words 'normal' and 'abnormal' in the way that they do, we will always be able to make statements like: 'It is normal to be a little abnormal' and 'It is highly abnormal to be completely normal.'

And, after all, such statements, while confusing, are also comforting.

CHAPTER SIX

PLANETS HAVE AN AIR ABOUT THEM

EVER since it was recognized that other planets existed besides our own, there has been considerable speculation concerning the possibility of life on these planets and on the kind of life that could be possible on them. Intimately bound up with such speculation are considerations of the kind of atmosphere that might be expected to surround a given planet. What do we actually know, or what can we reasonably speculate concerning planetary atmospheres?

Let's go about it in a systematic way, by considering first the raw materials of which a planetary atmosphere may be constructed. The various elements, which are the building blocks of any substance, atmospheres included, are available to different degrees. Some are more common than others and this must be taken into account. Common elements get first consideration in atmosphere building; the commoner, the better. After all, if you were told that for some certain purpose you could use either water or liquid radium equally well, you would be a most unusual character if you went further than the nearest water-tap to accomplish your purpose. And this 'principle of least action' is as applicable to the Universe as to you.

The comparative abundance of the more common elements in the universe as a whole (according to recent estimates) is given in Table XVI. The atoms of silicon are set arbitrarily equal to 10,000 and the quantities of atoms of other elements are given in proportion. What is at once obvious is that 90 per cent of the Universe is hydrogen (the simplest element) and 10 per cent is helium (the next simplest element). There is also about 1/6 of 1 per cent of impurities—meaning all the other elements.

It follows then that if you're going to collect a sample of interstellar gas and dust and make a sun or planet out of it, you're likely to end up with a big ball of hydrogen and helium.

That's what the sun is made of, for instance. It is 85 per cent

TABLE XVI

Atom Abundances in the Universe

Hydrogen	350,000,000
Helium	35,000,000
Oxygen	220,000
Nitrogen	160,000
Carbon	80,000
Silicon	10,000
Neon	9,000 (minimum)
Magnesium	8,700
Iron	6,700
Sulfur	1,000
All others	2,600

hydrogen and 15 per cent helium, plus a bit of impurity. (The shortage of hydrogen and excess of helium is due to the fact that for four billion years at least the Sun has been turning hydrogen into helium to keep shining.)

It's what Jupiter seems to be made of, too, if the most recent theories are more correct than previous theories have been.

Now that we have a list of the available materials, the next question is: Which of these are suitable for use in atmosphere-making? To be a component of an atmosphere a substance must be a gas or a volatile liquid (or solid) at the temperature of the planet's surface. (By a volatile liquid or solid I mean one which is in equilibrium with a substantial amount of its own vapor at the temperature being considered. For instance, at ordinary Earth temperatures, water is a volatile liquid and iodine a volatile solid. For that reason, water vapor is a normal component of Earth's atmosphere and, if there were enough iodine lying around, iodine vapor would be.)

Now we have quite a decent array of surface temperature in the planets of our own Solar System, and these are given for reference in Table XVII. The temperatures are given in degrees above absolute zero to avoid the complications of negative numbers.

TABLE XVII

Surface Temperatures of Planets of the Solar System in Degrees Above Absolute Zero

	minimum	maximum
Mercury (bright side)	450	650
Venus (bright side)	330	460
Earth	270	310
Mars	220	290
Jupiter	120	170
Saturn	90	130
Uranus	60	90
Neptune	50	70
Pluto	40	60

For comparison the boiling points of the common elements of the Universe are given in Table XVIII in degrees above absolute zero. Note to begin with that at no planetary temperature in the Solar System can carbon, iron, silicon or magnesium form part of any atmosphere. (The surface temperature of the sun is 6,000 degrees absolute and all these high-boiling elements *are* found in *its* atmosphere. This discussion, however, is concerned with planetary and not with stellar atmospheres.)

TABLE XVIII

Boiling Points of the Common Elements in Degrees Above Absolute Zero

Carbon	4,500
Iron	3,300
Silicon	2,900
Magnesium	1,380
Sulfur	718
Oxygen	90
Nitrogen	78
Neon	27
Hydrogen	20
Helium	4

Sulfur is not a gas at any planetary temperature either, but a substance often remains more or less volatile down to temperature 100 to 200 degrees below its boiling point and we can set 150 degrees below boiling as a kind of arbitrary limit for significant volatility. Sulfur would therefore be a volatile liquid at temperatures equalling Mercury at its hotter moments and sulfur vapor could then exist in the atmosphere.

The other elements are more likely substances for atmosphere-making. Oxygen is a gas out to Saturn and nitrogen is a gas out to Uranus. Both are volatile liquids on Neptune and volatile solids on Pluto. Neon, hydrogen and helium are gases even on Pluto. And since hydrogen and helium are overwhelmingly preponderant in the Universe as a whole, any planetary atmosphere must, *to begin with*, consist almost entirely of hydrogen and helium.

I say, *to begin with*.

There's a catch. In the gaseous state, the molecules of a substance don't stick together as they do in the liquid and solid state. Each molecule in a gas goes its own way at various speeds and in various directions, including up. There is always a thin trickle of gas continually drifting up and up and some molecules inevitably succeed in escaping from planetary bondage altogether. Atmospheres *leak*, in other words.

The size of the leak varies according to the size and temperature of the planet and is different for different gases. The smaller a planet is, the weaker its gravitational hold on the molecules, and the easier it is for the atmosphere to escape into space. The warmer a planetary surface is, the faster the molecules in its atmosphere move, and the more rapidly the atmosphere will escape into space. Smallness and warmth increase the atmospheric leak.

In addition, the smaller the molecules of a particular gas, the faster the average velocity of the individual molecules of that gas, and the more likely it is to escape into space. Hydrogen has the smallest molecule and helium the next smallest molecule of all known substances. The atmospheric leak is therefore largest for hydrogen and only a little smaller for helium.

Even a planet as large as Jupiter (317 times as massive as Earth and with a surface gravity $2\frac{1}{2}$ times as great) and as cold as Jupiter, may not be able to hold on to all its hydrogen. The hydrogen/helium ratio in Jupiter's atmosphere is only 3:1 instead of the 10:1 it is in the Universe as a whole. This means that if Jupiter has held on to all its helium, it has lost 2/3 of its hydrogen. (There is an alternative here which I must point out. It may be that helium with its lower melting and boiling points has been squeezed out to some extent in the body of Jupiter and that more of it has been forced into Jupiter's upper layers and atmosphere.)

Now Saturn, Uranus and Neptune are all smaller than Jupiter but all are colder, too, and the two effects cancel one another out. We can guess that all these (I leave Pluto out as an unknown quantity) have similar hydrogen-helium atmospheres and that, in fact, so do all planets that are large and cold.

As a matter of fact, though, hydrogen and helium are nearly impossible to detect spectroscopically at planetary temperatures. (At solar temperatures, they're very easy to detect, but that's another matter.) It was only quite recently and by rather indirect means that the hydrogen-helium nature of Jupiter's atmosphere was deduced. Before that, astronomers were much more aware of certain other components of Jupiter's atmosphere which, while present only in comparatively small quantity, happen to have strong absorption bands that are easily observed spectroscopically. What are these impurities?

Checking Tables XVI and XVIII, you might suppose that the chief impurities would be oxygen, nitrogen and neon in that order. You'd be right as far as neon is concerned. The chances are that it is present in Jupiter's atmosphere in a concentration of something below one per cent. You'd be wrong about oxygen and nitrogen, though.

Oxygen and nitrogen in the presence of a vast surplus of hydrogen would form compounds with the hydrogen, particularly under the pressure conditions in a large atmosphere. One atom of oxygen combines with two of hydrogen to form water (H_2O). One atom of nitrogen combines with three of hydrogen to form ammonia (NH_3). Water and ammonia would be more stable than oxygen and nitrogen themselves under hydrogen-helium atmosphere conditions.

Similar statements can be made for most of the other common elements listed in Table XVI. Helium and neon are out of it. They combine with no other element under any condition. They exist in splendid isolation. The others form hydrogen compounds if they can. If they can't, they form oxygen compounds, oxygen being the next most common compound-forming element.

Thus one atom of carbon combines with four atoms of hydrogen to form methane (CH_4). One atom of sulfur combines with two atoms of hydrogen to form hydrogen sulfide (H_2S). Silicon, magnesium, and iron won't combine with hydrogen. They combine with oxygen instead, forming silicon dioxide (SiO_2), magnesium oxide (MgO) and ferric oxide (Fe_2O_3) respectively.

Sulfur and carbon will combine with oxygen as well as with hydrogen. Oxygen is a lot less available than hydrogen, but both sulfur and carbon prefer oxygen to hydrogen by quite a bit, so a certain amount of sulfur dioxide (SO_2) and carbon dioxide (CO_2) would form (especially after much of the hydrogen has leaked away on smaller planets).

In Table XIX, are listed these common compounds and their boiling points in degrees absolute. (Incidentally, I should mention that the boiling points given in Tables XVIII and XIX are the values at Earth's atmospheric pressure. The values vary with pressure, going up as the pressure does as far

TABLE XIX

Boiling Points of the Common Compounds in
Degrees Above Absolute Zero

Magnesium oxide (MgO)	3900
Silicon dioxide (SiO_2)	2500
Ferric oxide (Fe_2O_3)	1800 (minimum)
Water (H_2O)	373
Sulfur dioxide (SO_2)	263
Ammonia (NH_3)	240
Hydrogen sulfide (H_2S)	213
Carbon dioxide (CO_2)	195
Methane (CH_4)	110

as what is called the critical point but no further. Let us use the ordinary values given in the tables to avoid complications. They will serve to compare one element or compound with another, and the line of argument would not be much affected by boiling point values that *would* take pressure into consideration.)

Looking at Table XIX, we see that magnesium oxide, silicon dioxide and ferric oxide could never form part of an atmosphere under any planetary conditions. On Earth, in fact, these three compounds, plus aluminum oxide (which boils at 2320 degrees absolute) form at least 80 per cent of the solid crust of the Earth.

Water would be a gas on Mercury, a volatile liquid on Venus and Earth (and on Mars at its warmest) but frozen solid and not volatile on the outer planets. Sulfur dioxide is in the same situation plus the fact that at Earth temperatures and below it tends to react with water to form an even less volatile compound.

Ammonia is a gas as far out as Mars and remains fairly volatile as far out as Uranus. The same for hydrogen sulfide and carbon dioxide. Methane remains a gas on Jupiter (always neglecting the pressure effect) and would be volatile even on Pluto.

As far as Jupiter is concerned then, the impurities in its atmosphere consist of ammonia, methane, carbon dioxide, neon and hydrogen sulfide; possibly in that order. Neon, like hydrogen and helium, is almost impossible to spot spectroscopically in the cold. Carbon dioxide and hydrogen sulfide are present in minor traces. That leaves ammonia and methane, and those are both easily detectable in Jupiter's atmosphere.

As one moves out from Jupiter, away from the Sun, to Saturn, Uranus and Neptune, the ammonia absorption bands get steadily weaker and the methane absorption bands steadily stronger. This is probably not due to any change in overall composition but only to the fact that as the temperature drops, ammonia becomes less and less volatile; there is less and less ammonia vapor in the atmosphere; and methane, which remains volatile all the way out, has less competition.

We can summarize then by saying that large, moderately

cold planets have hydrogen-helium atmospheres with ammonia as the chief impurity, while large, excessively cold
planets have hydrogen-helium atmospheres with methane as
the chief impurity.

But so far we have talked only of large planets. What about
small planets? What about the Earth?

To begin with, the Earth is closer to the sun than are any
of the large, outer planets and is therefore at a higher temperature. The molecules in its original atmosphere moved faster
than those on Jupiter and its colder brethren. Either Earth
could not collect the particularly nimble hydrogen and helium
in the first place, or, having collected them, she could not hold
them. In either case, Earth (and all the inner planets, for that
matter), were built up out of the 'impurities' of the Universe—
the elements other than hydrogen and helium.

This accounts for the great differences between the inner
and outer planets and explains why the inner planets are so
much smaller and denser than the outer ones.

Now one frequently thinks of the Earth, at its beginning, as
a molten globe that slowly cooled down and solidified. If this
were so, one would have to use most ingenious arguments to
explain the persistence of any atmosphere at all.

If, however, Earth were formed by gradual accretion of
matter in a turbulent maelstrom of interstellar material rather
than by way of a solar catastrophe, the original temperatures
(of Earth's outer crust, at least) might never have been startingly
higher at the beginning than now—say not above the boiling
point of water.

Let's suppose that and see where it takes us.

To begin with, let's consider the atomic or molecular weights
of the gases that are likely to occur in the Earth's atmosphere
originally. These are listed in Table XX. Remember—the
smaller the atomic or molecular weight, the more likely Earth
is to lose that particular gas.

The gases listed in Table XX fall into three groups. The light
gases, hydrogen, and helium, leak away or are never collected.
In either case they are not in Earth's atmosphere except in
minute traces. A second group, consisting of the heavy gases,

TABLE XX

Molecular (or Atomic) Weights of Possible
Atmosphere Components

Hydrogen	H_2	2
Helium	He	4
Methane	CH_4	16
Ammonia	HN_3	17
Water	H_2O	18
Neon	Ne	20
Hydrogen sulfide	H_2S	34
Carbon dioxide	CO_2	44
Sulfur dioxide	SO_2	64

hydrogen sulfide, carbon dioxide, and sulfur dioxide, would remain in the atmosphere even if Earth's surface temperature were rather higher than it is today.

The third group, methane, ammonia, water, and neon require more attention. At today's temperature, Earth could hold them. If the temperature were higher by 50 degrees they would slip away slowly. Judging from the molecular weights: 16, 17, 18, and 20, they ought all to slip away at the same rate, just about. This is not so; other factors intervene.

At a temperature of, say, 340 degrees absolute, water is still liquid and only a small portion of the substance is in the atmosphere as vapor and only that small portion is available for leakage. Methane and neon, on the other hand, are gases and are all available for leakage. Ammonia is in an intermediate position. It, too, is a gas, but it is a gas which is extremely soluble in water (while methane and neon are only very slightly soluble in water). Much of the ammonia is safely tucked away in the oceans where it is safe from leakage.

We can reason then that most of the methane and neon is lost; most of the water stays; and that ammonia is betwixt and between.

We end up with a planet which has an atmosphere composed mainly of ammonia and carbon dioxide, with hydrogen sulfide, and water vapor as minor impurities and with sulfur dioxide, methane, and neon present in traces.

We can summarize, then, the *only* types of atmosphere-structures that may be expected in the Universe on the basis of atom abundances alone:

(1) Large, excessively cold planets—Hydrogen/helium plus methane impurity (example, Neptune).

(2) Large, moderately cold planets—Hydrogen/helium plus ammonia impurity (example, Jupiter).

(3) Small, cool planets—Ammonia/carbon dioxide (example, early Earth).

(4) Small, hot planets—No atmosphere (example, Mercury).

(Note that I am omitting large, hot planets from consideration. No such thing is possible. Any planet close enough to a sun to be hot loses its hydrogen and helium and the elements that are left can only make a small planet.)

But if the atmospheres listed above are the only ones to be expected, that leaves out precisely the one type of atmosphere most important to us—the nitrogen/oxygen atmosphere on Earth today. How did that come about?

Well, the four cases listed above are those that may be expected on the basis of atom abundances *alone*. On Earth, a new factor enters in—the presence of life.

Life, in general, exists by making use of the energy that can be evolved from chemical reactions among the substances in its vicinity. Several possible schemes for doing this exist among the life-forms of Earth. There are life-forms that take advantage of energy-forming reactions among sulfur compounds, iron compounds and nitrogen compounds. Such life-forms never evolved past the bacterial stage. The raw materials they use for energy are too specialized.

The real success lay with those organisms that learned to extract energy from the most common substance on Earth—which happens to be water. (The lucky fellow who learns how to make delicious and nourishing soup out of sawdust is going to make a lot more money than one who learns how to make it out of peacock tongues.)

One type of organism (ancestral to the green plant) learned how to make use of solar energy to break up the water molecule into hydrogen and oxygen. The hydrogen was used to convert carbon dioxide (the second most available substance on early Earth) into starch and in this way solar energy was stored as chemical energy to be tapped as needed. The oxygen from the water was a by-product, not needed, and so was released into the air.

Observe that the net result, to the atmosphere, of this process (photosynthesis) is to consume carbon dioxide and to release oxygen. As the green plants multiplied and spread through the oceans and invaded the land, carbon dioxide was used up and oxygen produced at an ever greater rate.

There was the reverse tendency, too. When plant life died, the bacterial action involved in decay consumed oxygen and produced carbon dioxide. The development of animal life was also a factor in consuming oxygen and producing carbon dioxide. However, by the time equilibrium was established almost all the carbon dioxide was gone from the atmosphere (0·03 per cent of our modern atmosphere is carbon dioxide, no more). In its place was oxygen.

In the presence of this vast surplus of the active element, oxygen, any methane present was slowly converted to carbon dioxide and water. The water joined the oceans and the carbon dioxide was replaced by more oxygen through plant action. Hydrogen sulfide was converted to water and sulfur dioxide.

Finally, oxygen combined with the hydrogen atoms of the ammonia molecule to form water. The nitrogen atom of the ammonia molecule does not combine with oxygen except under drastic conditions and it went free to tie up in pairs as nitrogen molecules.

The result was that by the time equilibrium was reached and photosynthesis had completed its work of changing the atmosphere, both the carbon dioxide and the ammonia were gone. In its place was nitrogen (from the ammonia) and what was left of the triumphant oxygen. And so a new type of atmosphere must be added to the others:

(5) Small, cool planets, *with life*—Nitrogen/oxygen (example, modern Earth).

There remains, of course, the possibility of intermediate situations. For instance, a large planet with the proper temperature might have methane and ammonia in approximately equal concentrations in its atmosphere, and have a hybrid atmosphere intermediate between cases (1) and (2). Saturn and Uranus might be examples of such.

A planet of intermediate size and intermediate temperature, say one lying where the asteroid belt is now and somewhat smaller than Uranus in size, might lose most but not all of its hydrogen and helium and end up with an atmosphere in which hydrogen, helium, ammonia, methane, and carbon dioxide, are all present in respectable proportions. This would be a hybrid of atmospheres (1) and (3), of which there are no known examples.

A planet considerably smaller than Earth or considerably warmer might lose most of its atmosphere but not quite all, retaining a wispy kind of air rich in carbon dioxide. This is a hybrid of atmospheres (3) and (4) and an example of that is Mars (complicated by the possible presence of plant life).

Finally, a planet might be in the process of developing life, with some of the carbon dioxide and ammonia consumed and free oxygen and nitrogen appearing in the air. This is a hybrid of atmospheres (3) and (5) and there are no known examples.

I have now covered, as far as I can tell, every type of atmosphere that there is any likelihood of encountering anywhere in the Universe.

Any *reasonable* likelihood.

Let us, however, throw off the shackles of probability and devote some attention to atmospheres that are, in the main, wildly improbable.

Life depends, as I said, on the utilization of energy. The way this is handled on Earth, stripped to its bare essentials, is this:

Plants, utilizing solar energy, split water to hydrogen and oxygen, storing the hydrogen (in the form of compounds) in their tissues. Animals (and plants, too, for that matter) make use of the chemical energy of the stored hydrogen. Animals eat food which consists of plant tissue or animal tissue derived from plant tissue and combine its hydrogen with the oxygen they breath. In other words, we have a cyclic water/hydrogen-oxygen system. Plants push in one direction and animals in the other, the whole remaining in balance.

Furthermore, one of the members of the system is a liquid present in sufficient quantities to form oceans and one of the others is a gas forming a major portion of the atmosphere. So let's say that in order to have life-as-we-know-it, we need a cyclic system with one member a liquid and another a gas.

What other systems are possible? Is there anything we can substitute for oxygen? Something, which like oxygen will produce energy if combined with hydrogen and something which is a gas and which produces a liquid on combination with hydrogen.

Well, to substitute for oxygen it has to be an active chemical and the only low-boiling elements that will bear comparison with oxygen as far as activity is concerned are sulfur, chlorine, fluorine and bromine. To give you an idea of the kind of pickle we're in, Table XXI gives the atomic abundance of these substances in comparison with oxygen (on a silicon equal to 10,000 basis).

TABLE XXI

Atom Abundances of Oxygen and Possible Substitutes

Oxygen	220,000
Sulfur	1,000
Chlorine	21
Fluorine	3
Bromine	0·5

From Table XXI, you can see at once how improbable it is that the atom distribution over sizable volumes of space should be so abnormal as to create planets in which sulfur, chlorine, fluorine or bromine are the major components of the atmosphere in the place of oxygen.

But we'll ignore that and just consider the cyclic systems that result. They are:

    (a) Hydrogen sulfide/hydrogen–sulfur
    (b) Hydrogen bromide/hydrogen–bromine
    (c) Hydrogen chloride/hydrogen–chlorine
    (d) Hydrogen fluoride/hydrogen–fluorine

In Table XXII, some data are given on the components of these systems.

TABLE XXII

Temperatures Ranges for Gas-Liquid-Solid States of Various Substances

Sulfur	393 to 718
Hydrogen sulfide	190 to 213
Bromine	266 to 332
Hydrogen bromide	187 to 206
Chlorine	172 to 239
Hydrogen chloride	162 to 188
Fluorine	50 to 86
Hydrogen fluoride	190 to 293

Note: Each substance named is liquid between the two temperature values in (degrees absolute), solid at temperatures below the lower value, and gaseous at temperatures above the upper values—atmospheric values assumed.

If we take sulfur first, we can see from Table XXII (and Table XVII) that sulfur is a gas not even under extreme Mercurian conditions, and that at any temperature at which sulfur is gaseous, hydrogen sulfide is *certainly* gaseous. However, who says it is sulfur that has to be the gaseous component of the cycle. At any temperature between 393 and 718 (which covers the normal temperature range of Venus as well as Mercury) it is possible to have a hydrogen sulfide atmosphere and a liquid sulfur ocean.

The same inversion holds true in the cases of bromine and chlorine. Neither a bromine nor chlorine atmosphere is admissable since in both cases there would be no liquid component of the cycle. Hydrogen bromide and hydrogen chloride would also be gaseous. But at a temperature range of 266 to 332 (Earth and Mars), one could have a hydrogen bromide atmosphere and oceans of liquid bromine; while at a temperature range of 188 to 239 (asteroid belt) one could have a hydrogen chloride atmosphere and oceans of liquid chlorine.

In all three cases plants would have to breathe in hydrogen sulfide (or hydrogen bromide or hydrogen chloride), break it up to hydrogen and sulfur (or bromine or chlorine), store the hydrogen in their tissues and excrete liquid sulfur (or bromine or chlorine). Animals would have to eat the plants and drink the liquid sulfur (or bromine or chlorine) reform the hydrogen sulfide (or hydrogen bromide or hydrogen chloride) and belch it out periodically.

This may sound complicated and unpalatable to you but the big drawback is that when hydrogen and chlorine combine they yield only one-third the energy that the combination of hydrogen and oxygen does. Hydrogen and bromine yield only one-eighth as much and hydrogen and sulfur only one-tenth as much. Life is such an energy-consuming thing that that alone should eliminate the bromine and sulfur system (at least for anything over the micro-organism stage) and make the chlorine system pretty shaky.

Fluorine is another thing altogether. No inversion is necessary here. At temperatures between 190 and 293 (Mars), it is possible to have a fluorine atmosphere and a hydrogen fluoride ocean, and fluorine combines with hydrogen to yield $1\frac{1}{2}$ times as much energy as the hydrogen-oxygen combination would produce. This seems the best bet (if we could only forget how rare fluorine is in the universe compared to oxygen).

But there's a catch. Fluorine yields a big helping of energy on combining with hydrogen and that means that it is that much more difficult to break up hydrogen fluoride into hydrogen and fluorine.

Plants on earth break up water by using the energy of red light. To break up hydrogen fluoride, red light would not be energetic enough. Blue light would be necessary; perhaps even the near ultra-violet.

This makes things tricky. If the sun is close enough or hot enough to provide this more energetic light in sufficient quantity, it might make the temperature of the planet hot enough for a hydrogen fluoride ocean to be impossible. If the sun is far enough or cool enough to allow the hydrogen fluoride ocean to exist there might not be enough energetic radiation to allow fluorine-type photosynthesis to take place.

In all these cases, by the way, the effect on the composition of tissue constituents is profound, but I am deliberately neglecting that. I'm not even thinking about it. That's for some other occasion some other day. Sufficient unto *this* day are the atmospheres thereof.

So far, we have been replacing the oxygen atoms of our familiar water-oxygen cycle. What if we leave them alone and replace the hydrogen atoms instead. Sulfur is the only substitute I can think of. In the range from 393 to 718, we can have a sulfur dioxide atmosphere and a liquid sulfur ocean. Plants would breathe in the sulfur dioxide, break it up into sulfur and oxygen and store the oxygen in their tissues.

Animals would eat the high-oxygen plants, drink the liquid sulfur and belch out sulfur dioxide. The beauty of this is that the combination of sulfur and oxygen yields as much energy as the combination of hydrogen and oxygen.

Another possibility involves not an element but a compound, carbon monoxide (CO). Carbon monoxide will substitute for hydrogen since it will combine with oxygen to form carbon dioxide, yielding sufficient energy, too. The only trouble with that is that carbon dioxide is a liquid over only a very small temperature range, 20 degrees or less and then only under pressures at least 5 times as high as that of our own atmosphere. Arranging to have a carbon dioxide ocean is too tricky to be practical.

This may cause you to think what about using other and more complicated compounds—a carbon monoxide, formaldehyde system; or a cyanogen–hydrogen cyanide system. Well, the more complicated you make a system, the more you'll have to sweat justifying it, and the less likely you are to meet it anywhere in the universe. The same goes for systems where both hydrogen and oxygen are replaced.

I will leave the problem of making up atmospheres at *that* level of complication and improbability to the reader.

I would like to mention, though, before leaving the matter, one atmosphere system, that I think is more probable than any I have yet mentioned in this speculative half of the chapter.

The system is a *reverse* water/hydrogen-oxygen system.

Imagine a planet the size of Uranus in the position of Mars. It has just managed to hang on to enough hydrogen to allow it to be a major component of the atmosphere, along with ammonia, methane and carbon dioxide, and yet the planet is just warm enough to allow the presence of liquid water.

Plant life on such a world might split water to hydrogen and oxygen. It would then combine oxygen and methane (which it breathes) to form starch, liberating the hydrogen into the atmosphere. The methane would be replaced by hydrogen ; the carbon dioxide would be reduced to methane and then replaced by hydrogen; the ammonia would stay put. The atmosphere of the world would end as only hydrogen and ammonia.

Animals would eat the starch, breathe the hydrogen; re-combine the oxygen of the starch with the hydrogen to form water, and breathe out methane gas.

Our situation, exactly, but in reverse.

With which thought, and with my head humming slightly, I'll step out into the back-yard to take a deep, invigorating breath of oxygen and stare fondly at the grass which is so busy making more of it.

CHAPTER SEVEN

THE UNBLIND WORKINGS OF CHANCE

THE question for discussion is exactly how much luck was involved in the development, on Earth, of life from non-living substances, and, as a corollary, what chance there is of finding life on any other Earth-like planet.

To go about this systematically, let us first decide what (from a chemical standpoint) non-life is, and what (from a chemical standpoint) life is, and then, perhaps, we can see how non-life may turn into life.

Non-life first—and specifically the ocean.

The ocean consists, chiefly, of course, of water. Secondly, it contains dissolved ions (that is, electrically charged atoms or groups of atoms). The chief ions are sodium ion and chloride ion, but substantial quantities of potassium ion, calcium ion, magnesium ion, sulfate ion, phosphate ion and others are also present. These are all substances that exist in the ocean today and, we have every reason to believe, existed in the ocean before life began, though probably in lesser concentration then.

But the primordial ocean contained more than water and ions. It contained gases in solution, derived from the atmosphere. So does today's ocean, to be sure, but the primordial atmosphere was different from today's atmosphere and the dissolved gases in the primordial ocean were different, therefore, from those in today's ocean.

The nature of the atmosphere of the primordial Earth in the days before the coming of life was discussed in the last chapter. The conclusion was that Earth's atmosphere then consisted primarily of ammonia (NH_3) and carbon dioxide (CO_2). Ammonia is extremely soluble in water and carbon dioxide is fairly soluble. Both gases would occur in quantity in the ocean.

Minor constituents of the early atmosphere would be hydrogen sulfide (H_2S), methane (CH_4) and perhaps even some hydrogen (H_2) which had not yet had time to leak away into space. Of these, hydrogen sulfide is somewhat soluble, but the other two are only slightly soluble in water. Still there is so much water in the ocean, that the total dissolved quantity of even a slightly soluble gas comes to volumes that must be measured in cubic miles.

There we have non-life. The substances mentioned in this section are the non-living raw materials of life.

Which means I must now turn to life.

The living cell (of the human being, say) is an exceedingly complex mixture of substances, any one of which, if isolated in a test-tube, is no longer alive, or at least does not possess the properties we commonly associate with life. This might lead us to believe that life is something more than a chemical or a group of chemicals—and to a certain extent, I suppose that is correct.

Yet not entirely correct. Some of the chemicals in the cell are more nearly associated with life than are some others. For instance, in the interior of the cell is a denser portion, marked off from the rest by a thin membrane. This denser portion is called the cell nucleus. It is the cell nucleus which organizes the growth and reproduction of the cell so that if we were to try to pin life down to something smaller than the cell, it would be at the nucleus that we would have to look.

Within the nucleus there is chromatin material which, during cell division, coalesces into a number of threadlike objects called chromosomes. There is a tremendous quantity of evidence to the effect that it is these chromosomes that determine the chemical characteristics of the cell of which they form a part. During cell division, each chromosome duplicates itself meticulously so that each daughter cell gets a full set of accurate chromosomes.

It becomes reasonable to suppose that life is most closely associated with the chromosome portion of the cell. As material evidence for that, consider the sperm cell, which is just a tiny, tailed bag, containing a half-set of chromosomes and nothing else. Yet not only is the sperm cell alive but it carries within it the chemicals controlling the thousands of hereditary characteristics that are transmitted from father to child. (The other half-set of chromosomes is contained in the ovum so that father and mother contribute equally to the chemical characteristics of the child.)

We can go further still. The chromosomes (on the basis of indirect, but extremely detailed and convincing, evidence) are strings of genes, each gene controlling an individual inherited characteristic. (To supply a musical metaphor, the individual gene strikes a single note; while all the genes of all the chromosomes of an individual cell sound the complex symphony we call life.)

The gene, we think, is a single molecule; extremely complex, it is true, but still a single molecule of the type known as nucleoprotein.

And that is as far down as we can trace life within a cell.

Let's try another tack. So far we have been looking deeper and deeper into a complex cell. Suppose that instead we look for simpler and simpler cells. Would that help?

Unfortunately, simple cells don't exist. Animals that are smaller and less 'advanced' than man may have fewer cells and fewer different kinds of cells and less specialized cells, but each individual cell remains just as complicated (chemically) as ever. Even the single cell of the bacterium is not simple. It is, if anything, more complicated than the cells of a human being, and contains all the different kinds of chemical substances a human cell does.

But there are objects which are subcellular in size, yet which are considered to be alive. Those objects are the viruses.

Viruses come in a variety of subcellular sizes. The larger viruses are still fairly complicated and contain a variety of chemicals, but as one considers smaller and smaller viruses, they appear to strip themselves of one type of chemical after another, hanging on, presumably to the more essential, then, finally, only to the most essential.

The smallest viruses of all are made up of single molecules of one particular substance—nucleoprotein.

So we reach life-at-its-simplest by two routes and come up with genes in one case and viruses in the other, and both are nucleoprotein.

Do nucleoproteins possess any properties which mark them out from other chemicals? Is there anything about them to suggest why they should be so intimately connected with what we call life?

In one respect there is. Nucleoproteins, in their natural surroundings, have the ability to reproduce themselves. The genes within the cell, for instance, can somehow cause simpler substances in the surrounding fluid to line up in such a way that atom for atom the final arrangement resembles the atom arrangement in the molecule composing the gene. This line of simpler substances is then knit together to form one huge, complicated molecule—the duplicate of the gene which served as a pattern. This is called autoreproduction and, of all known substances, only the nucleoprotein is known to possess the property.

The gene can bring about the synthesis, not only of a second molecule of itself, but also of somewhat less complicated molecules (perhaps modeled on limited portions of itself) called enzymes. These enzymes govern the chemical reactions within the cell and, in this way, dictate the cell chemistry. Each gene is responsible for the production of a few specific types of enzymes (perhaps even of only one type of enzyme).

The virus can be looked upon as an independent gene (or group of genes) which can invade cells and run them to suit itself. It is like the cuckoo which lays its eggs in the nests of other birds. The virus, within a cell, superimposes its own chemistry, by some means, upon the cellular victim. It forms its own type of enzymes and duplicates itself over and over again out of the simpler substances within the cell, and all the cell's normal functions are suspended indefinitely under the stress of the foreign demands.

The method by which a nucleoprotein multiplies itself and 'grows', must be distinguished from the way in which a crystal 'grows'. As a solution of sodium chloride slowly evaporates, sodium chloride crystals form and increase in size. They increase in size because as sodium ions and chloride ion come out of solution, they align themselves on existing crystals according to the pattern of electrical charges on the crystal surface. There is no change in the ions in the process. They were ions in solution and they're ions in the crystal. They're bound to one another by the same forces that bound them in solution. It is just that there is order in the crystal where there was none in solution. There is *increased organization* in the crystal.

The nucleoprotein molecule, however, does not merely find more nucleoprotein molecules in its neighbourhood to add on to a conglomeration of itself. It starts with different substances altogether, much simpler than itself, and brings about the formation of another 'itself'.

The increase in organization involved in a nucleoprotein duplicating itself is much higher than that involved in a crystal of sodium chloride growing larger.

In fact, one might try to define the 'livingness' of a substance or conglomeration of substances as a measure of the rate at which it can increase the organization of its surroundings and the level of organization it can reach.

Now, then, we can come to a conclusion. If we can deduce how a nucleoprotein molecule might have been formed from non-living material—even just one nucleoprotein molecule— then all the rest of the development of life from that single nucleoprotein becomes understandable.

To paraphrase a famous saying: Nucleoprotein is the whole of life; all else is commentary.

We've managed to define the problem in its simplest terms, now. On the side of non-life, we have a lot of water, considerable carbon dioxide and ammonia, a small quantity of hydrogen sulfide, and a bit of methane and hydrogen, plus the ions in the ocean. The atoms included in the molecules of these substances are a lot of hydrogen atoms, a considerable number of carbon atoms and oxygen atoms, a sizable number of nitrogen atoms and a small number of sulfur atoms. Among the ions are phosphate ions which include phosphorus atoms.

On the side of life, we have nucleoprotein, the molecules of which consist of a large number of hydrogen atoms, a considerable number of carbon and oxygen atoms, a sizable number of nitrogen atoms and a small number of sulfur atoms. Also a small number of phosphorus atoms.

If we just look at the kind of atoms in non-life and in life, or even at the relative proportions of the kinds present in both cases, there isn't much difference. But when it comes to the relationship among the atoms——·

On the non-life side we have small molecules made up, at the most, of five atoms apiece. On the life side we have tremendous nucleoprotein molecules made up of millions of atoms, each placed just so.

The question is, how did the atoms in these small molecules manage to place themselves just so in order that the first nucleoprotein molecule might be formed ? Once one nucleoprotein molecule exists, it can guide the formation of others. But how was the *first* one formed?

Could it have been the result of the blind workings of chance? Could the atoms have just happened to bump one another and stuck together in the right pattern—just by chance, after a billion years of random trying.

To test the blind-chance hypothesis, let's set up the simplest possible analogy. Suppose we had marbles of six different colors and suppose we took a few million assorted marbles and threw them helter-skelter into a box. Suppose each marble were coated with a kind of cement which would make it stick firmly to any other marble it happened to touch. Having thrown them into the box, pull the whole sticking-together mess out. What are the chances that, just by luck, just by the blind workings of chance, all the colored marbles have so arranged themselves that a pattern equivalent to that of a perfect nucleoprotein is the result.

Having read Chapter Three, you may be able to make a shrewd guess as to what the answer to that one is. For those of you who have not, I will only say that the chances are more infinitesimal than you or I can imagine. So infinitesimal, that if the known universe were crammed with nothing but people and each person performed the test twenty times a second (a hundred times a second, a thousand times, what's the difference!) for a billion years (or a trillion or a trillion trillion), the chances of any one of those humans coming up with a perfect nucleoprotein pattern at any instant in all that time is still infinitesimal.

This kind of thing was pointed out, rather triumphantly, by

Lecomte du Noüy, in a book named *Human Destiny*, published in 1947. His point of view was that this proved it to be completely unreasonable to suppose that life had originated by the blind workings of chance and that therefore there *must* have been some directing intelligence behind its origin.

The de Noüy argument had quite a vogue (and still has) among people who approved the conclusion and were willing to overlook flaws in the line of reasoning for the sake of that conclusion. But, alas, the flaws are there and the argument contains a demonstrable fallacy.

Let's take a simpler case and see if we can spot the fallacy.

Suppose we start with a mixture of the gases, oxygen and hydrogen. By heating them, we can cause the molecules of oxygen and hydrogen to combine with one another with explosive eagerness. The result is a substance made up of molecules consist of both hydrogen and oxygen atoms, three atoms altogether, arranged in a V-shape.

So far, all this is true, but suppose that all this is *all* you know. Nothing else! What, then, if you start working out what the final molecule might be on the basis of the blind workings of chance? You know that the final molecule contains three atoms, including both hydrogen and oxygen. There are six kinds of combinations that fulfil that condition. Those are:

H–H–O	H–O–H	O–H–H
O–O–H	O–H–O	H–O–O

H–H–O is equivalent to O–H–H (just turn one molecule around and you have the other) and O–O–H is equivalent to H–O–O. Each can be formed in two different ways, you see, so H–H–O and O–O–H are both twice as probable as are either H–O–H or O–H–O, each of which can be formed in only one way.

If, then, oxygen atoms and hydrogen atoms combine at random to form three-atom molecules containing at least one of each, then the laws of probability state that in any number of such three-atom molecules, the most probable distribution of each variety is as follows:

H–H–O	1/3
O–O–H	1/3
H–H–O	1/6
O–H–O	1/6

Having combined oxygen and hydrogen, we ought now to test theory by observation. Suppose we're super-microscopically small and can take out, from the mass of final substance, ten individual molecules, at random, and inspect them closely.

What are the chances that *all ten* happen to be H–O–H, without a single one of the other varieties present. The chances are, 1 out of 6 x 6 x 6 x 6 x 6 x 6 x 6 x 6 x 6 x 6 or about 1 out of 60,000,000. (Work it out yourself, if you don't believe me.)

Suppose you picked out twenty molecules, what are the chances that all twenty are H–O–H. The answer is 1 out of 3,600,000,000,000,000.

You are welcome to figure out the chances of picking out ten billion molecules at random and finding them all H–O–H. The chances are as infinitesimal as are those of manufacturing a nucleoprotein molecule by pure luck.

And yet—— If you pick out ten billion molecules of the product of hydrogen-oxygen combination, you will find that all of them *are* H–O–H. There are *no* O–O–H, O–H–O, or H–H–O molecules included.

What's wrong then? Are the laws of probability in error? No. It's the people who think they are using the laws of probability that are generally in error.

I started off, you see, by assuming that any three-atom combination of hydrogen and oxygen atoms was equally probable. My entire argument was based on that. My exact words were: 'If then, oxygen atoms and hydrogen atoms combine at random——'

And that's the point. We have no right to assume they combine *at random*, and, as a matter of fact, they don't. The chemical properties of the hydrogen and oxygen atoms are such that the combination H–O–H is the only one that has any reasonable probability at all, so it is the only combination formed.

The same fallacy exists in the du Noüy type of argument.

Sticky marbles can stick together any old way and form any old pattern but that is no guide to the behavior of atoms. Atoms, real atoms, can only form a limited number of combinations with one another, and of that limited number, some are more probable than others.

So one does not and must not ask: what are the chances that a nucleoprotein molecule is built up through the blind workings of chance?

One must ask: what are the chances that a nucleoprotein molecule is built up through the known laws of physics and chemistry—the very definitely unblind workings of chance?

To consider the possibilities, let's take the nucleoprotein molecule apart.

It can be done easily enough. All the really complex molecules made by living tissue are polymeric in nature; that is, they are made up of simple units, or atom-combinations, that are repeated over and over in a chain. The units are called monomers. In some cases, as in starch or in cellulose, there is only one type of unit making up the molecule. In the case of nucleoproteins (or proteins in general) the units vary.

In general, the large molecules of living tissue can be broken down to the smaller units that compose them by adding the atoms of a water molecule at the joints between the units. This is called hydrolysis. The units can recombine by splitting out the water molecules. This is called condensation.

Under the proper conditions, large molecules can hydrolyze into smaller units, and smaller units can condense into large molecules, either way.

For instance, the nucleoprotein of a living virus can be hydrolyzed into two parts: one, the protein part, and the other a nucleic acid part. Neither part by itself is living nor has any of the infectious characteristics of the original virus. If the two parts are mixed together and allowed to remain so for a while, a certain amount of recombination takes place. Either the number of possible ways of recombining is not very great, or else the 'correct' way is more probable than others because by the 'blind workings of chance', fully one per cent of the recombinations proved to be the original virus once more with all its infectious characteristics. (This was an actual experiment and, in a way, it represents the man-made creation of life out of non-life.)

Well, then, if it can be shown that the simple molecules, water, carbon dioxide, ammonia and so on can form the units out of which nucleoproteins are built up by condensation, then a large step has been taken.

What are the units which are involved? Without going into the chemistry, Table XXIII gives the names and some idea of the variety of these units.

TABLE XXIII

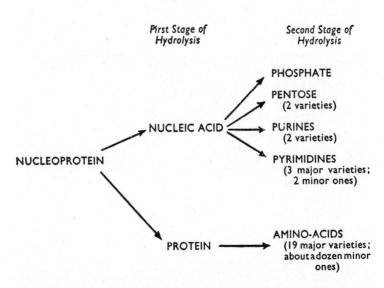

Of these, the phosphate group exists as such in the ocean. It is an inorganic grouping scarcely more complicated than ammonia or carbon dioxide, so we don't have to worry about it at all. The pentoses, purines, pyrimidines and amino-acids are all moderately complicated, their molecules being made up of from 10 to, at most, 30 atoms apiece. And they are good, stable compounds; nothing fancy.

Let's concentrate on the amino-acids. They are the most various of the groups and the most complicated, in some ways.

Suppose we mix water, ammonia, carbon dioxide, methane, hydrogen sulfide, and hydrogen and sit down and wait for amino-acids to be formed.—Bring lunch with you because you'll be waiting a long time. Amino-acids won't be formed in a billion years or a trillion or a trillion trillion. Just mixing is not enough.

You see, in general, complicated molecules have more energy content than simple molecules. For simple molecules to be built up into complicated ones, energy must be added.

In other words, water will not run uphill unless it is pumped. A rock will fall upward only if thrown. A scattering of bricks will come together to form a house only if someone takes an interest.

In turning water, ammonia, etc. into amino-acids, the chemicals are moving uphill and that won't happen unless, somehow, they are made to do so. Or, to be more precise, energy is supplied.

Does that mean we have to abandon the unblind workings of chance after all? Not if we can find a source of energy that just happens to be hanging around the primordial earth where all this is happening.

And we can! In fact, we can find two sources.

One source of energy sufficiently concentrated to force chemical reactions to take place that wouldn't otherwise—is the lightning bolt.

The lightning bolt is with us today and it works. Our modern atmosphere contains nitrogen and oxygen. Nitrogen and oxygen can combine to form nitrogen oxides, *if* a lot of energy is supplied. The energy of a burning match isn't enough (luckily!) The energy of the lightning bolt is. During the instant of flash, a small amount of nitrogen and oxygen in the air immediately surrounding it are forced together to form nitrogen oxides. These dissolve in the rainwater to form nitric acid. When the nitric acid hits the soil, it combines with compounds existing there and forms nitrates.

Now the amount of nitrogen oxides formed by an individual lightning flash is infinitesimal and the amount of nitric acid in rainwater wouldn't hurt gossamer, but take it over the entire

Earth and you have something. It has been estimated that about 250,000 tons of nitrates are formed by thunderstorms each day, and that this is a significant factor in maintaining soil fertility.

All right, then, the primordial lightning had no nitrogen and oxygen gas to play with, but it did have molecules of ammonia, carbon dioxide, methane, hydrogen sulfide, hydrogen, and, of course, water vapor for playthings, and it slammed them together most energetically.

In 1952, a chemist named Miller circulated a mixture of ammonia, methane, water, and hydrogen past an electric discharge for a week, trying to duplicate primordial conditions. At the end of the week, the mixture was analyzed by paper chromatography (*see Chapter Four*) *and amino-acids were present in the mixture*. They were not the product of life-forms; the system had been carefully sterilized. They were not there to begin with; that had been checked. They had been formed from simpler compounds and energy. To be sure, only two or three of the simplest amino-acids were detected, but then Miller had only waited a week and he had a good deal less than a whole atmosphere of gases to play with.

You may wonder, though, if thunderstorms and lightning-bolts existed on the primordial Earth. It seems hard to believe they didn't, but let's suppose that they didn't. Does that knock everything to pieces?

It does not. There's a second source of energy that no one can possibly deny existed—the ultra-violet radiation of the sun. Experiments have been conducted in which simple compounds have been subjected to ultra-violet radiation and more complicated compounds have been formed.

To be sure, amino-acids have not yet been reported in the ultra-violet experiments, as far as I know. One of the reasons for that is that they haven't yet included ammonia among the compounds being subjected to the energy, to my knowledge, and without the nitrogen of ammonia, amino-acids can't be built. You can't have cake without flour.

In any case, the principle that ultra-violet will drive compounds uphill is definitely established.

Picture, then, the primordial ocean, as simpler compounds

are converted into more complicated compounds under the lash of ultra-violet and of lightning. Amino-acids, purines, pyrimidines, pentoses and many other types of compounds can be formed and as time passed they would thicken the ocean into a soup. As more and more of them were formed, they would collide with one another more and more frequently, and with energy spurring them on, they would frequently stick together.

But mind you, they would *not* stick together in a random manner. There would always be a limited number of ways in which they could stick together, sometimes not more than two or three ways.

For instance, a purine or pyrimidine could combine with a pentose and a phosphate in not more than six or eight likely ways to form what are called nucleotides.

Two nucleotides could combine with one another in not more than three likely ways, or two of the simpler amino-acids could combine with one another in not more than two likely ways, to form double molecules.

A double molecule may collide and combine with another nucleotide or amino-acid to form a triple molecule and so on. When enough of these units combine, the multiple amino-acids have become protein and the multiple nucleotides have become nucleic acid. And then, finally, the day will come when a nucleic acid molecule and a protein molecule will collide and stick together in such a way as to form a nucleoprotein—a nucleoprotein sufficiently complicated and properly constructed to be able to autoreproduce.

And when that happens, we have life.

The mark of those chance encounters exist in the proteins and nucleic acids of today. We have learned how to determine the order of amino-acids in the proteins and the order of nucleotides in nucleic acids. Where we have actually done so, the order appears quite random.

Of course, you may wonder how amino-acids and nucleotides, put together at random, can turn out to serve the needs of life so neatly. It seems too much to ask of chance. There is an intellectual trap here; we tend to put the cart before the horse.

There were all the oceans and up to a billion years as the

space and time in which nucleoproteins (and other molecules) might form at random (within the limits, always, of the laws of physics and chemistry). All that space and all that time, multiplied a millionfold, would not suffice to make the formation of a *particular* nucleoprotein more than infinitesimally probable; that is, one with particular amino-acids and nucleotides arranged in a particular order.

But if we are counting on the production of any old nucleoprotein with any old arrangement of parts, the time and space is more than sufficient. To be sure, every different order of parts makes for a final molecule with a different set of properties, but, so what? Whatever the final properties, those will be the raw materials of life. Some nucleoproteins might have properties that make for better survival? Those will survive.

To suppose that the properties of the chemicals within living tissue are adapted to the needs of living tissue, rather than vice versa, is what I meant by putting the cart before the horse.

It is as though we congratulated Nature on placing ears where she did on the human head, since that was just the right distance for the ear-pieces of spectacles to fit round. Or to be grateful that the rotation of Earth has been so designed as to last exactly 24 hours to the second, thus making a convenient whole number to work with. Or to wonder why the sun is wasted by having it shine in the daytime when it is light anyway, rather than in the night when it is dark and we could use a little light.

But let's move on. There are two final points to consider. Can life still be created out of non-life by natural processes on Earth today? Can we suppose that life may be created out of non-life on planets other than Earth?

To answer the first question, there seem to be very good reasons indeed for doubting that the process can be repeated today.

First, as life advanced to the stage where photosynthesis became possible and oxygen and nitrogen replaced the ammonia and carbon dioxide of the atmosphere, some of the oxygen was converted by the impinging ultra-violet into the more energetic ozone. (Ordinary oxygen molecules are made up of two oxygen atoms apiece; ozone molecules of three. Again ultra-violet light is converting the simple into the complex.)

The ozone thus formed absorbs ultra-violet strongly, with interesting consequences. In today's atmosphere, for instance, there is a layer of ozone fifteen miles up, formed by the ultra-violet impinging on the upper atmosphere. That layer absorbs ultra-violet and prevents it from reaching the surface of the Earth. A good thing, too, because modern life, not adapted to ultra-violet light, probably could not survive if the U–V came crashing through. Nevertheless, the rays of the sun that hit our modern oceans are comparatively weak and tame and much less efficient at producing complicated molecules out of simple ones.

Again, the lightning bolt has only nitrogen, oxygen and water vapor to work on in our modern atmosphere and the nitric acid produced is not a stepping stone on the way to life. Missing are the large quantities of carbon atoms (in carbon dioxide) and hydrogen atoms (in ammonia) that were present in the primordial atmosphere. Without carbon and hydrogen, life as we know it cannot form though all Jove's thunderbolts flashed at once.

Does this sound unduly pessimistic? Are there no sources of life-yielding energy other than the sun and the storm? Is Nature so unresourceful as to yield no third possibility or am I so unimaginative as not to see one?

Unfortunately, whether there are other sources of energy or not doesn't matter. There is another difficulty of another type that puts the final quietus on present-day formation of life from non-life.

The primordial ocean was a *dead* ocean. Large molecules could slowly be built up in peace and thicken in concentration till the oceans were practically nothing more than a nutrient broth. Nowadays, though, any organic molecule that happened to come into existence through some fortunate collision of simpler molecules would promptly be absorbed by some minute sea-creature and either broken down for energy or incorporated into living tissue.

The modern ocean teems with life, and long before new life could possibly be formed, the raw materials out of which it might have been formed would be gobbled up voraciously by the life that already exists.

Now what about other planets?

Proposition 1 : Given a planet at a distance from its sun such as to give it a temperature in the range where water is a liquid at least part of the time, then (barring exceedingly unusual characteristics of the interstellar stuff out of which the planet is formed —either in quantity or in the abundance of the elements) then an ammonia–carbon dioxide atmosphere is inevitable.

Proposition 2 : Given an ammonia–carbon dioxide atmosphere and a source of energy such as the ultra-violet light from the sun, life is inevitable.

It follows, then, if the line of deductions is reasonable, that life exists on any Earth-like planet. (Note, I say nothing about humanoid life, or even intelligent life. I say, simply—life. About anything beyond that, I make no predictions. Nor am I saying anything about anything resembling life which may exist on a completely different chemical basis from our own—non-nucleoprotein life, in other words—on such planets as Jupiter or Mercury.) Is there any way of checking this conclusion?

There is one partial check we can make. We have a variety of worlds in the Solar System and among them is one world, other than Earth, which fulfils the conditions set above—just barely. That world is Mars. (Venus might be another, but we know practically nothing about it.)

Mars is almost too small to suit, but it manages to retain just a bit of atmosphere and water. It is almost too cold to suit, but water just manages to be liquid part of the time. It is almost too far from the sun to suit, but it picks up some ultra-violet from the sun (less than half of what the primordial Earth did).

So Mars is a severe test of our line of reasoning. A cold, nearly dry, nearly airless world—— We could excuse ourselves if it failed.

But let's see, is there life on Mars?

Despite all the odds against it, despite the poorness of the planet, the answer seems to be : possibly, yes. At least, the green areas on Mars seem to signify some kind of vegetation. The vegetation might be very primitive and undiversified, nothing like the teeming life of Earth, but it would be *life*.

And if Mars can do it, then it is my belief that any Earth-like planet can do it.

CHAPTER EIGHT

THE TRAPPING OF THE SUN

THE first and greatest discovery by man was the use of fire. That discovery, more than anything else, was the point at which he was raised from beast to man.

The Greeks recognized the importance of the discovery and viewed it as a gift of the demi-god, Prometheus, who stole fire from the sun and brought it to naked and shivering man. To the Greeks, fire was a piece of the sun, trapped and made tame, bent to the use of man.

If for 'sun', you say 'energy', the Greeks were right.

When man learned to start a fire by rubbing two sticks together, he put at his own disposal, for the first time, a source of energy other than that contained in his own body. It was because man, with fire, had more energy at his disposal than had any other animal in creation that he became something more than animal.

But man's discovery some thousands of years ago was only an echo of a similar and even greater discovery made by a primitive bit of life perhaps a billion years ago.

In the previous chapter, we left life a nucleoprotein molecule adrift in the primordial ocean. It was alive, but it had no source of energy but what happened to come its way. (It was like a man who had to wait for lightning to hit a tree before he could count on a bit of fire.)

In this chapter we consider the way in which a microscopic organism anticipated Prometheus by a billion years and, to raise itself to higher estate, stole the fire of the sun.

Let's begin the story with ourselves here and now. Our body makes use of energy constantly. Our muscles contract. Our nerves carry electrical impulses. Our kidneys filter our blood stream. Our cells manufacture complicated molecules out of simple ones. All these things take energy. Where does it come from?

We can be specific and take a chemical reaction such as the union of two amino-acids to form what is called a dipeptide. The dipeptide can join up with a third amino-acid to form a tripeptide; that with still another to form a tetrapeptide; then a pentapeptide; a hexapeptide; a heptapeptide; and so on indefinitely (or at least as far as your knowledge of Greek numeral prefixes will allow you to).

When enough amino-acids have combined with one another, a protein molecule is formed, so this type of reaction is the very basis of life. Without it, a nucleoprotein molecule could not duplicate itself out of the raw materials about it and without *that*, there could be no life.

Yet there is a catch. Two amino-acids, if brought together, will not combine of their own accord. A dipeptide contains more energy than two amino-acids separately. Every time another amino-acid is pushed into line and bound to the peptide chain, the energy of the peptide is increased. That energy must come from somewhere.

The amount of energy that has to be put into the assembling of each amino-acid varies from 0·5 kilocalories per mole to 4·0 kilocalories per mole, depending on the particular amino-acid involved. (If you happen to know what a 'kilocalorie per mole' is, I am happy for you. If not, it doesn't matter. Just keep your eye on the numerals.)

The body gets the energy it needs for this and almost all other similar jobs from 'high-energy phosphate bonds' present in its tissues (and in all living tissue).

There are certain compounds, you see, the molecules of which contain a phosphate group (made up of a phosphorus atom, two hydrogen atoms and four oxygen atoms, $-OPO_3H_2$) that hangs on rather precariously to the rest of the molecule. The chemical bond between the phosphate group and the rest of the molecule is taut, in a manner of speaking, ready to give with a bang. When the phosphate group does break off, nearly 5 kilocalories per mole of energy are turned loose. That is more than enough energy to tie any two amino-acids together.

The high-energy compound most used by the body for such jobs is called adenosine triphosphate. This compound carries no less than three phosphate groups in a line and we can write it A-P-P-P for short. Sometimes one phosphate group is knocked off, sometimes two.

When the A-P-P-P breaks up, part of it sticks to an amino-acid in the vicinity and forms a high-energy amino-acid complex. The complex now contains enough energy to be able to attach itself to another amino-acid without trouble and while it is doing that, it lets go of the piece of the phosphate it was holding. That leaves a dipeptide. Repeat the process over and over and a protein can be built up.

If all this wordage has you frowning just about now, try Figure 15, which says the same thing more schematically.

The only trouble with all this is that someone is bound to ask: and where does the body get its high-energy phosphates from? After all, for every amino-acid stuck on to a peptide

Figure 15. How a High-Energy Phosphate works.

a—In the absence of high-energy phosphates:

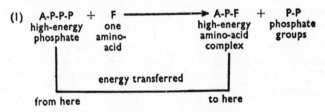

b—In the presence of high-energy phosphates:

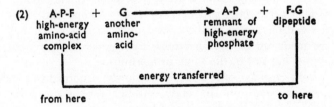

chain, one high-energy phosphate goes down the drain, and the body's supply of such phosphates is exceedingly limited.

Obviously, the body has to make high-energy phosphates as fast as they are used up—but how? To stick a phosphate group back on to the molecule from which it was broken requires just as much energy as was released by the original break; that means nearly 5 kilocalories per mole. (In matters of energetics, remember this above all: you can't get something for nothing. That's called the First Law of Thermodynamics.)

Well, if the body has trouble putting amino-acids together at 4 or less kilocalories per mole a throw, how will it manage when faced with finding 5 kilocalories per mole?

It seems there is another type of chemical, which biochemists have only grown to appreciate quite recently, called an acyl mercaptan, in which the key group of atoms is made up of a carbon, an oxygen, and a sulfur—(CO)–S. The acyl mercaptan is even more energetic than the high-energy phosphate. When the (CO)–S combination is broken, a little over 8 kilocalories per mole are let loose.

That's enough to form a high-energy phosphate bond.

Only—and you're ahead of me, I know—where do the acyl mercaptans come from? The body makes them, but how? Now it has to find 8 kilocalories per mole to put an acyl mercaptan back together again. (It's like the question that used to plague me when I was young. You need tools of a particularly hard steel alloy to shape ordinary steel objects. Then you need tools of a harder steel to shape the hard-steel tools. Then you need tools of a still harder steel to shape—— You get the idea.)

To see where the acyl mercaptans come from, we have to consider the food we eat.

Our food consists of a number of kinds of compounds but, as far as energetics is concerned, the two important classes are the carbohydrates and the fats. Both carbohydrates and fats are made up of carbon atoms, hydrogen atoms, and oxygen atoms, but not in the same proportions.

Both carbohydrates and fats are slowly combined with oxygen (*i.e.* 'oxidized') in the body, through dozens of steps, until nothing is left but carbon and hydrogen atoms combined with all the oxygens they can hold. The final products are carbon dioxide (CO_2) and water (H_2O).

We can summarize by writing the following:

> Carbohydrates (or fats) plus oxygen gives rise
> to carbon dioxide and water

But carbohydrates and fats contain more energy than do the carbon dioxide and water molecules to which they give rise. The energy left over in the conversion is turned loose so that we should really write the following:

> Carbohydrates (or fats) plus oxygen gives rise to
> carbon dioxide and water *and energy*.

This last bit is obvious if carbohydrates or fats are strongly heated. Fats will begin burning. Carbohydrates will char first and then glow and burn slowly. Both will be converted to carbon dioxide and water and the energy released will be given off in the form of heat and light.

The same quantity of energy, not an iota more nor an iota less, is given off when the carbohydrates and fats are combined with oxygen in the body. The chemical pathway of change in the slow oxidation in the body is radically different from that of the rapid burning in a flame, but the energy developed in either case is the same. (It's the First Law of Thermodynamics again.)

The big difference is that oxidation in the body, being slow, is under control. The energy given off is not in the form of a dancing flame pouring heat and light uselessly into space. Instead, the energy is given off in little spurts that are captured in neat packets in the form of high-energy compounds.

The crucial step in oxidation within the body is the combination of hydrogen and oxygen. The hydrogens that occur in a molecule of fat or carbohydrate (or which are stuck on in the course of the chemical changes they undergo) are combined with oxygen—two hydrogen atoms for each oxygen atom. Every time two hydrogens are removed from a molecule and combined (via a number of steps) with an oxygen, 45 to 65 kilocalories per mole are released. This is more energy than even an acyl-mercaptan bond represents; 6 to 8 times as much.

However, the energy of such a hydrogen-oxygen combination within the body is put into the formation of only two to four high-energy phosphates.

The energy changes in the known steps from the food we eat to the protein built up in our tissues is shown schematically in Figure 16.

2 hydrogen atoms from the fat and carbohydrate we eat combine with an oxygen atom from the air we breathe and	yield	45 to 65 kilocalories per mole
This is enough to form 2 to 4 acyl mercaptans which, on splitting,	yield	16 to 32 kilocalories per mole
This is enough to form 2 to 4 high-energy phosphates, which, on splitting,	yield	9½ to 19 kilocalories per mole
This is enough to form 2 to 4 amino-acid hookups which, on splitting,	yield	1 to 16 kilocalories per mole

Figure 16. Energy Statistics in the Body.

Figure 16 should make one point clear that some people manage to scramble rather badly.

It is the long experience of mankind that everything tends to run down. Clocks stop, iron rusts, water runs downhill, living creatures age and die, the hills weather and erode into sand, the earth's rotation is slowing, the sun is using up its hydrogen.

This is an important and universal rule—that everything is gradually running down—and scientists call it the Second Law of Thermodynamics.

Some people have been impressed by the fact that life seems to have a contrary effect. A human being can wind a stopped clock, resmelt rusted iron, pump water uphill again, rejuvenate age by giving birth to young and so on. There is the feeling that there is something in life which is not subject to this running-down rule and therefore something which makes it superior to the laws of physics or chemistry.

Not so.

It is all very well to point out that man can take a lump of iron ore and a mess of bauxite and sand and clay and make steel beams and aluminum and glass and bricks out of them and put them altogether to make a beautiful skyscraper. This is 'building up' rather than 'running down',—*it seems.*

But in order to bring this about, man has had to use a mess of energy in the form of burning coal to smelt the iron ore and fuse the sand and bake the clay and make the electricity that will separate the aluminum out of the bauxite. And human energy has had to be used, too. All this burning coal and sweating humanity represents a 'running down' that is much greater than the 'building up' involved in making the skyscraper.

Our whole civilization depends on the running down (as fast as possible) of the energy content of the coal and oil reserves of the world. And the running down of these reserves and the energy they represent is much greater than the building up we manage to do as a result. It can't be helped. The Second Law of Thermodynamics has never been broken yet.

See how Figure 16, now, shows the way in which the human body runs down. You start with 45 to 60 kilocalories per mole when a pair of hydrogen atoms are united with oxygen. You end up with two to four amino-acid links which represent an investment of 1 to 16 kilocalories per mole. You're building up your protein—at a 1 to 16 rate. You're running down your food—at a 45 to 65 rate. Anywhere between 65 and 98 per cent of the energy of your food is just wasted. It is given off as heat and if you work hard, you will yourself note that one of your body's chief concerns is to get rid of all the heat that is being produced at the same time that some work is being turned out.

Since evaporating water will absorb heat, the body is designed to perspire. On humid days, when water will not evaporate very well, you feel completely miserable. It's not the heat, you say, it's the humidity. But it *is* the heat, just the same; the body heat you are developing and don't want and can't get rid of fast enough.

Not only we, but all living creatures get by on the energy developed by converting carbohydrates and fats to carbon dioxide and water. All organisms use a small bit of the energy and throw the rest away. But then where does the supply of carbohydrates and fats come from? In a billion years or so, we haven't run out.

We, and other creatures as well, make our own, of course, but that scarcely counts since the energy required to make it come from energy developed by oxidizing carbohydrates and fats to begin with. And since you can't beat the Second Law, the amount of carbohydrate and fat you must run down to get energy is greater than the amount you can build up with that energy.

And it's no use saying you get your fat or carbohydrate from milk, or beef, or eggs, or poultry or pork because cattle, chickens, and pigs are busy burning carbohydrates and fats much faster than they are storing them in their own tissues or in eggs and milk.

No, if we are to have life continue for more than a short time, we must find a way of creating carbohydrates and fats by some method that doesn't use up carbohydrates and fats. A new source of energy must be found.

The green plant does the trick; it has trapped the sun. It has found a way of taking the energy of sunlight and using it to break the water molecule into hydrogen and oxygen. (The energy required to break the water molecule is about 65 kilocalories per mole, but to manage the trick, the plant has to use probably 100 kilocalories per mole of light energy; possibly up to 200 kilocalories per mole. The Second Law wins out again, but fortunately the supply of sunlight is virtually endless.)

Some of the separated hydrogen and oxygen recombine to liberate enough energy to form three high-energy phosphates for every molecule of water re-formed. These high-energy phosphates are used to supply the energy that will enable the rest of the hydrogen to combine with the carbon dioxide of the air to form carbohydrates and fats. Figure 17 presents the process (called 'photosynthesis') in schematic form.

Notice that photosynthesis represents almost the exact reverse of the process that goes on in our body. In our body, it is:

Carbohydrates (or fats) plus oxygen yield carbon dioxide
plus water plus chemical energy.

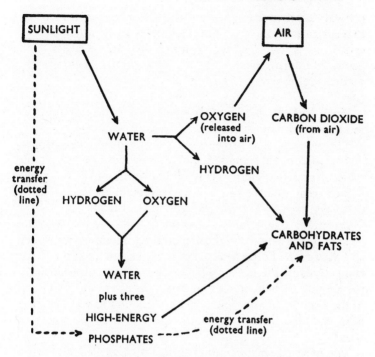

Figure 17. Scheme of Photosynthesis.

In the green plant, during photosynthesis, it is:

Carbon dioxide plus water plus solar energy yield
carbohydrates (or fats) plus oxygen.

The oxygen produced and the carbon dioxide used up in
photosynthesis changed the atmosphere from its primordial
composition of ammonia and carbon dioxide to the present
composition of nitrogen and oxygen.

To summarize then, green plants convert solar energy into
chemical energy, and their cells then live upon the chemical
energy stored in carbohydrates and fats.

All animal life lives upon this chemical energy, too, either by
eating plants or by eating animals that have eaten plants, or by
eating animals that have eaten animals that have eaten plants,
and so on. No matter how many animals can be forced into the

one-eats-another chain, at the bottom is some green plant and that supports all the rest. This includes sea-life, where the one-celled plants, called algae, swarm in the surface layers of the ocean and form the foundation upon which rests all other marine life from worms to whales.

How does all this apply to the lonely little nucleoprotein molecule adrift in the primordial ocean.

The only chemical property we know it must have had is the ability to construct another molecule of itself out of simpler molecules such as amino-acids. But tying amino-acids together takes energy. Where did the nucleoprotein molecule get the necessary energy? From carbohydrates and fats?

Probably! The ocean was swarming with organic molecules formed by the action of lightning on the primordial atmosphere and the action of ultra-violet rays from the sun upon the simple compounds in the ocean. The end result must have included the simpler carbohydrates and fats. *But* there was no oxygen in the primordial atmosphere. The first step in getting energy is to combine the carbohydrates and fats with oxygen. Well, then?

The most common solution to this problem involves a process known as glycolysis. In glycolysis, a molecule of glucose (a simple sugar) which contains 6 carbon atoms, 12 hydrogens and 6 oxygens is split (via a number of steps) into two molecules of lactic acid, each made up of 3 carbons, 6 hydrogens and 3 oxygens. Enough energy is released by this split to form 2 high-energy phosphates.

Glycolysis is inefficient in comparison with the complete oxidation of glucose to carbon dioxide and water. That complete oxidation would give rise to no less than 32 high-energy phosphates. But glycolysis has this advantage: *it doesn't require molecular oxygen.* Even today, when there is plenty of oxygen in the air, tissues sometimes make use of glycolysis when the demands for energy are greater than the rate at which oxygen can be supplied. Muscles, when engaged in active work, make use of glycolysis. Embryonic tissue, which is chronically short of oxygen, makes use of glycolysis to a certain extent.

Presumably, then, the primordial nucleoprotein molecules made use of glycolysis to make their high-energy phosphates and got along without molecular oxygen.

But how does the nucleoprotein bring about all the necessary changes? How does it split glucose molecules and make high-energy phosphates and split those and combine amino-acids and so on? It is so easy to say 'the nucleoprotein does this and the nucleoprotein does that', but *how* does it do it?

Which brings us to the question of catalysis.

There are a great many reactions which take place readily when the conditions are right, which take place scarcely at all when the conditions are not right.

For instance, suppose it was vitally necessary for you to make a certain notation and you had both a pencil and a piece of paper in your possession. Suppose, however, you were standing in the middle of a vast and featureless plain, built of undulating sand. You would have nothing to rest the paper on and you could make your notation only with great difficulty and probably not very legibly.

Suppose, however, a flat board of some hard smooth material suddenly appeared. Using that to write on, you would have no problem. The job could be done quickly and well.

Now you used the board neither to write with nor to write upon directly. It simply offered you a surface on which what you wanted to do could be done. Further, it was in no way used up. If you had a trillion notations to make on a trillion pieces of paper, the same board could be used for all, given enough time.

The writing board is an example of a catalyst.

There are molecules or conglomerates of molecules which do not take part in a chemical reaction but which offer surfaces upon which that chemical reaction can take place speedily. Protein molecules are particularly good for this purpose because their surfaces are so varied from spot to spot.

Every protein of respectable size contains at least 19 different kinds of amino-acids, dozens of each, perhaps. Each kind of amino-acid is made up of different combinations of atoms and even when they are bound together to form proteins, portions of them, known as 'side-chains', are present on the surface of the protein molecule.

These side-chains vary in several ways. Some are made up of carbon and hydrogen atoms only. Some of carbon, hydrogen and oxygen; or carbon, hydrogen and nitrogen; or carbon, hydrogen and sulfur. Some have an electrical charge on them and some have not. Of those with an electrical charge, some have a negative charge and some a positive.

The result is that the surface of a protein, any protein, has a particular pattern of atoms and of electrical charges.

A molecule which could be involved in some type of reaction may happen to find on some portion of the protein surface a kind of atom and charge distribution which just fits its own. It snuggles in and forms a 'complex'. Such a complex (for reasons I can't go into now) reacts more easily than the molecule alone would.

For this reason, a molecule which would seem perfectly aloof ordinarily, would, upon hitting the appropriate portion of a protein molecule, instantly undergo changes. It might break apart or pick up a molecule of water or transfer some of its atoms to another compound or any of a million different things.

A protein with such a surface is a catalyst and such proteins are called enzymes. The human body contains thousands of different enzymes, each of which catalyzes one particular reaction or one particular kind of reaction.

A protein formed at random by the chemical processes discussed in the previous article would have a vast number of different types of patterns on its surface. None of them might be suitable for any useful reaction. On the other hand, some of them might be.

It's like those multi-bladed pocket-knives that used to be fashionable; the ones that carried screw-drivers, awls, knives, scissors, corkscrews, files, can-openers and things for taking pebbles out of horse's hooves. If you had a job to do, you might find a blade that would do it and you might not. The greater the number of blades and the greater the variety, the better your chances.

Well, with a nucleoprotein containing a million amino-acids, the chances of finding a spot on the molecule where a reaction involving the splitting of glucose could be catalyzed were not completely negligible. And maybe another spot could catalyze the formation of an acyl mercaptan, and still another the formation of a high-energy phosphate.

It may be that millions of nucleoprotein molecules were formed before one was found with the proper surface patterns. Only that 'proper' nucleoprotein molecule could develop the energy to form another nucleoprotein molecule and only that nucleoprotein molecule would be 'alive'.

We can see now that in order for a nucleoprotein molecule to reproduce itself it must break down appropriate molecules in the ocean about it; the complex molecules that had been built up by the action of the sun's ultra-violet rays to some point short of life. This would be the nucleoprotein molecule's 'food'.

And as the nucleoprotein molecules duplicated and reduplicated, the strain on the 'food' supply would be ever greater. The ocean would begin to be scoured clean of complex organic molecules as some of them would be converted to simpler compounds for energy purposes and the rest would be built up into nucleoprotein, these joining the ravenous horde and looking for food in its turn.

Eventually, an equilibrium would be reached. The nucleoprotein population would remain at a number where the rate at which the organic material was consumed would be just equal to the rate at which it was produced by the random effect of solar energy. Since the rate at which ultra-violet light produced organic compounds was probably slow indeed, the nucleoprotein population of the ocean would have to be very low.

Furthermore, if things continued in that fashion, it would have to remain low for as long as life existed. Life would be only a rare phenomenon of the ocean surface—a scavenger molecule living on the occasional sugar molecule it happened to bump into.

To progress further than that, one thing was necessary—the capacity for change; and that, fortunately, the nucleoprotein molecule possessed.

In the course of this book, I have said several times that the nucleoprotein had the capacity of causing molecules of the simpler units that composed it to line up next to it until an atom for atom duplicate was built up. Each individual unit is probably lightly bound to the corresponding unit that forms part of the nucleoprotein molecule. The individual units are then knit together strongly and the new nucleoprotein molecule is released.

Now the nucleoprotein molecule doesn't want such a duplicate built up. It has no consciousness as far as we know and no desires. It is just that a symmetrical arrangement, like-next-to-like, is the stablest possible arrangement (due to something called resonance) and therefore the most probable arrangement. However, the most probable arrangement is not that which occurs always; it is merely that which occurs most often. Occasionally, a less probable lineup of units occurs. At longer intervals still, a still less probable lineup, and so on.

For instance, if unit A and A^1 are fairly similar, it will happen once in so many duplications that an A^1 will line up next to an A in the nucleoprotein molecule. The resulting molecule will be an A^1 modification. When the modified molecule duplicates itself, an A^1 will line up next to the A^1 and another A^1 modification will be produced. In this way, different series of nucleoprotein molecules will be continually coming into existence.

Imperfect duplications are not the only changes that take place. The nucleoprotein molecules are being continually bombarded with the sun's ultra-violet light and with cosmic rays and with gamma rays from radioactive materials. Every once in a while, a quantum of such radiation will strike a nucleoprotein molecule in such a way as to change the arrangement of its atoms somewhat. If it remained still capable of duplication, it would duplicate this new arrangement.

In either case, when a nucleoprotein molecule changes its structure for any reason and passes that change on to its 'descendants', the process is known as a mutation.

Now consider the mutated nucleoprotein. With a new unit in place, the pattern of atoms and charges on its surface is changed in at least one spot. Its catalytic properties may be changed if that one spot is a catalytic spot. It may be that it loses a vital ability as a result and can no longer develop the energy necessary to duplicate itself. In that case it is no longer 'alive' and can serve only as food for its more fortunate companions. This is probably the result of most mutations.

Occasionally, though, a mutation occurring entirely by chance, may actually improve the catalytic ability of a vital spot, or form a catalytic spot on the surface where no such spot existed before. Such a mutated molecule might have the ability to utilize its food more efficiently, use energy less wastefully, reproduce itself more quickly. Whatever it is, the new molecule may displace and crowd out the old ones.

You will notice that this is a form of molecular evolution exactly similar to the evolution on a larger scale with which we are familiar. (In fact, the evolution that leads from lizards to birds and from tree-shrews to man is just a reflection of the tiny molecular changes going on in the nucleoproteins of the genes of these creatures.)

In what directions can this molecular evolution go? Judging from what we see about us now, one of the directions must have been toward the development of an ability for several nucleoprotein molecules to form a more or less permanent union with one another.

You can see the advantage of such co-operation. A single nucleoprotein molecule must be able to catalyze all the necessary reactions involved in self-duplication; all without exception. As soon as one ability was lost, the molecule was dead. If several such nucleoproteins banded together, the loss by one molecule of a particular catalytic ability was no longer fatal. The others in the chain still possessed it. Furthermore, as time went on, each gene might begin to specialize in certain of the catalytic abilities or even in one only and do that one with particular efficiency.

The more complex viruses that exist today may actually consist of as many as 25 nucleoprotein molecules (or genes, as we may now call them) in close co-operation. The human cell, it is estimated, has somewhere between 2,000 and 14,000 genes.

Another direction in which molecular evolution took place was in the formation of a protective membrane about the nucleoprotein molecule (or molecules). In some way, the nucleoprotein molecule managed to collect a film of fatty molecules about itself. This film was 'semi-permeable'; that is, it let some molecules through and not others, depending on the size and chemical properties of the molecules.

For instance, such a membrane would not let protein molecules through and that made possible the invention of enzymes.

You see, the nucleoprotein molecule could reproduce itself only when all the necessary units were in line. But what if only a portion of the units could be found at a particular time. In that case, only a fraction of the molecule could be formed. It wasn't alive, this fractional molecule, and it just drifted away to be food for some other nucleoprotein molecule.

Yet this might easily represent a waste, since the portion of the nucleoprotein molecule that had been duplicated, might have been one of the catalytic spots.

Once the nucleoprotein molecules had surrounded themselves with a membrane, though, such incomplete fragments could not escape, and the fragments would serve as detached catalytic spots; as enzymes, in short.

In this way, the nucleoprotein would be able to 'delegate authority'. It would no longer have to do everything itself, but could create any number of enzymes to take care of the individual reactions that needed catalysis, while it alone remained 'alive'.

The cell nucleus, which is surrounded by a membrane separating it from the rest of the cell, and which contains the genes, may be the direct descendant of these primordial nucleoprotein sacs. It is interesting to note that the cell nucleus (even of our own cells) is incapable of handling molecular oxygen. It has no enzymes fit for the purpose. It gets its energy only by glycolysis—as though it had evolved in an atmosphere that lacked oxygen.

All of this would increase the efficiency of life's use of what organic molecules could be found in the primordial ocean, but it wouldn't increase the supply.

In order for life to advance, the cells had to guide the formation of new organic matter. It had to make sure that such formation was not simply the result of chance collisions of sunlight and molecules. It had to trap the sun. It had to create a molecule which could absorb solar energy and transfer it to high-energy phosphate bonds.

The deed was accomplished. How long it took we have no way of knowing. The key molecule was chlorophyll, which is made up of a porphyrin ring system and a magnesium ion. The materials were common enough. The porphyrin ring system is very stable and was probably swarming in the primordial ocean just as were other stable organic molecules. And magnesium ion is one of the commonest in the ocean.

Apparently, then, a nucleoprotein molecule was formed through random mutation which could form an enzyme out of one of its catalytic spots which could latch on to such a chlorophyll molecule and put it to use.

Any nucleoprotein sac that developed such an enzyme was fortunate indeed. All such a sac needed was water, carbon dioxide, certain simple ions and sunlight. All these were inexhaustible and now the nucleoprotein sacs required the drifting food of the ocean surface no longer and could multiply almost without limit.

But in order to do so, one more invention was required—cells. The nucleoproteins could form their own carbohydrates and fats now but once formed there was a tendency for them to drift away. To be sure, the nucleoprotein molecules might be content simply to fill the oceans slowly with food, as it had been filled in the beginning. Perhaps this was what happened at first, but obviously it is an inefficient process.

Then it must have happened that one sac developed a second membrane about itself, further away than the first membrane. Between the two membranes food might now be stored.

As the nucleus formed a glucose molecule it would travel out through the inner membrane into the space between the membranes. Or if the cell (as we may now call it) bumped into a glucose molecule floating in the ocean, that glucose molecule would travel in through the outer membrane into the space between the membranes.

In either case, in the space between the membranes, a phosphate group would be added to the glucose and its properties would be so changed that it could no longer cross the films again. It would be trapped within the cell. Once enough sugars were collected, they could be hooked together to form a starch molecule, and starch could be converted into the still more concentrated energy store represented by fats.

You see, by storing starch and fats, the cell could make sure it profited from its exertions and didn't distribute the sweat of its brow, so to speak, over the vast reaches of the ocean.

Naturally, the outer portions of the cell, called the cytoplasm, had to possess enzymes with which to catalyze the reactions involved in forming starch and fat and breaking them down when necessary, too. For that reason, a new type of nucleo-protein molecule was developed which is characteristic of the cytoplasm and which can also duplicate itself and make enzymes.

The cytoplasm may have been developed after photo-synthesis had continued long enough to place some oxygen in the atmosphere, because it is the cytoplasm of the cell that has the capacity to utilize molecular oxygen.

Chlorophyll-containing cells, which we may now call plant cells, multiplied extensively and filled the oceans once again with food—in the form of cells rather than of individual mole-cules. Cells without chlorophyll could now develop which could live, parasitically, on the food painstakingly stored by the plant cells.

Such animal cells, as we may call them, could engulf plant cells whole, strip them of the energy of their food content and build up their own store of carbohydrates and fat. They, in turn, could be the prey of still other cells.

Animal cells, making use, as they did, of plant cells, did not depend on the presence of light. They could spread into deeper layers of the ocean.

When plants invaded the land, they were tied to their roots, because they had to have a lot of water continuously. Animals let the plants worry about that, ate the plants, and developed independent locomotion.

Plants had to build up their food supplies slowly and were sessile, inert things. Animals broke down plant food (or other animal food) rapidly and had enough energy to develop active muscles and nerves capable of concentrating electric charges and carrying sensory impulses.

That meant, eventually, the development of a nervous system, and of a brain. That, in turn, meant that some day intelligence could be achieved and a creature like man would evolve, a creature capable of wanting and trying to puzzle out how it had all come about.

CHAPTER NINE

THE SEA-URCHIN AND WE

IN any free association test, the chances are appreciable that the word 'evolution' will evoke the response 'fossils'. And fossil remains are usually of bones, teeth, shells, scales and other hard parts of a body. Evolution, as most of us think of it, is thus largely a history of morphological change (that is, changes in shape) of the hard parts of the body, plus what can be deduced therefrom (which is often precious little) about the soft parts.

We've got the shape of the hard parts neatly categorized from the trilobite to the Neanderthal. We can trace the steps in the morphological development of the horse, the elephant and man in a series of skeletal gradations. See any museum of natural history.

But think of the questions morphology can't answer. Did Eohippus have any vitamin requirements the modern horse does not have, or vice versa? Did Neanderthal man utilize his amino-acids in any way differently from us? What, precisely, was the clotting mechanism involved in the blood of Tyrannosaurus Rex?

Barring time-travel, we'll never know. But we might be able to make reasonable guesses, perhaps, if we study and compare the biochemistry of the various living species that exist today.

Biochemical evolution is less spectacular than morphological evolution. A morphological invention such as wings has been made at least four independent times (insects, pterodactyls, birds and bats) in four different styles, but biochemical inventions are usually made once, or if more than once, then in identical style. The uses to which the various B vitamins are put were decided very early in the game and all living cells today, from bacteria to those of man, use them in the same way. There are many other examples of the biochemical uniformity of life despite tremendous morphological variations.

But uniformity isn't universal. Biochemical differences

among species do exist and then things become really interesting.

Take the case of fat digestion among mammals. Fats are one of the major food components and an important body fuel. To be utilized by the body, the fatty substances in food must first be digested by the action of enzymes in the intestines. There is one catch. Fats are not soluble in water and digestive fluids are mostly water. Fats will not be digested with anything approaching efficiency unless something is done to enable them to mix with the watery digestive fluids.

The answer is found in the liver secretion known as bile. The bile, which is discharged into the small intestines, does not itself contain digestive enzymes but it does contain substances known as bile salts. The bile salts consist of molecules with double-jointed solubility properties. One half of the molecule is similar to fats in its structure and that half will dissolve in fats. The other half contains groups of atoms that are soluble in water.

In order to satisfy both halves of itself, bile salt molecules group themselves along the surface where fat and water meet. In this way, the fatty portion can face the fat and dissolve in it, while the rest can face the water and dissolve there. Both halves of the molecule are happy. The more surface between fat and water that there is, the more bile salt molecules can be made happy. One way in which the amount of surface can be increased is to distribute the fat through the water in the form of small bubbles. The smaller the bubbles, the more surface there is for a given weight of fat. The addition of bile salts to a mixture of water and fat thus encourages the formation of such small bubbles.

Bile salts are, in this manner, the body's natural detergents. They homogenize fats in the intestines, and the tiny bubbles that result mix well with the watery digestive fluids and can be attacked by enzymes.

There are two main varieties of bile salts, differing in the chemical structure of the water-soluble half. In order to avoid going into the chemical details, we will simply call the two varieties the G-salts and the T-salts. Both exist in the biles of various animals. Both do their detergent job adequately. In one respect, though, they behave differently. There is a fat-like substance called cholesterol which the G-salts don't seem to handle very well. The T-salts, however, homogenize cholesterol perfectly.

Now, in general, herbivorous animals (plant-eating) are particularly strong in G-salts and poor in T-salts. This is all right because plants are less fatty on the whole than animals are and what plant fat does occur is quite poor in cholesterol. Now since the G-substance, out of which G-salts can be made, is present in quantity in all cells, whereas the T-substance is present in much smaller amounts, why bother manufacturing T-salts that you can do without. So herbivorous animals stock up on G-salts and do well.

The animal fat, however, that forms part of the diet of carnivorous (meat-eating) animals is rich in cholesterol. The bile of carnivorous animals is rich in T-salts. Those animals need it and even though the T-salts are more difficult to scrounge up in quantity, they do it.

Now where does man fit in? Man is a member of the Primate order, which runs from the lemurs to himself and includes the apes and monkeys. All primates, with only one exception, are herbivorous, or, at most, will eat insects. The one exception, of course, is man himself. Homo sapiens is omnivorous in fact (that is, he will eat anything he can digest and a few things he can't) and carnivorous by choice.

Man has adapted himself to this kind of diet as far as morphology is concerned, but what about this biochemistry? His bile is still the bile he has inherited from his mainly herbivorous primate ancestors and is rich in G-salts and poor in T-salts, so though his diet is full of cholesterol, he lacks the equipment to handle it properly and keep it in solution, or at least well-mixed with water.

You ask: So?

So is there any connection between this and the fact that Homo sapiens is the one species that is plagued with gall-stones, which are conglomerations of cholesterol (usually) that has precipitated out of the bile little by little? Is there any connection between this and the fact that Homo sapiens is the one species that is plagued with atherosclerosis (our number one killer these days) which consists largely of the deposition of cholesterol little by little in the walls of the arteries?

Is there? I honestly don't know. The argument as I've presented it sounds good, but biochemistry these days is, in many ways, but the hand-maiden of medicine. Few biochemists devote themselves to the workings of various species except where some definite problem of immediate interest to Homo sapiens is concerned. Therefore not enough is known about various animal biles and their manner of working to make the above argument airtight. So far, it's just a speculation which I've come across.

Can biochemical evolution affect the morphological evolution with which we are familiar? Maybe. We can try on some more speculation for size.

All animals produce a compound called uric acid as a waste product, some producing more than others. Birds and reptiles, for instance, produce uric acid in quantity as one of their main waste products. (I'll have more to say about that later.) They have special ways of getting rid of it and we can forget them for now. Mammals produce only small quantities of uric acid, but its disposal raises a problem.

The logical way for mammals to get rid of uric acid is to dump it into the urine. The trouble is that uric acid is quite insoluble so it takes a lot of urine to get rid of a little bit of uric acid. Most mammals don't even bother, but bypass the problem completely. They have an enzyme called uricase, which breaks up uric acid to a substance named allantoin. Allantoin is considerably more soluble than uric acid and can be dumped into the urine without trouble. That ends the problem.

Or at least it ends it for other mammals; not for man. Man and the anthropoid apes differ from all other mammals in not having uricase. (There is a variety of dog, the Dalmatian coachhound, which seems to be low in uricase, but it has some.) Any uric acid which is formed in man or ape stays uric acid. It must get into the urine as best it can since it can be eliminated only in that way. If too much gets into the urine for the latter to hold, it will precipitate out and form one variety of kidney stone. If there's too much even to get into the urine in the first place, it may precipitate out in other parts of the body, beginning usually with the joint of the big toe, and the condition known as gout results.

Since man and apes share this problem, the loss of uricase must go far back in time to a point where the human stock had not yet diverged from that of the anthropoid apes, unless you're willing to believe that man and each species of ape have separately and coincidentally lost their uricase, which I'm not.

The question is, why should the enzyme, uricase, have been lost? To be sure, in one way, there doesn't have to be a reason. Mutations take place in haphazard fashion, and are usually for the worse. But then, mutations for the worse generally don't survive in the long run; only mutations for the better (in the sense of better fitting the environment). If some pre-anthropoid had lost the enzyme, uricase, would not he and his descendants have been at some disadvantage because of their extra propensity for joint troubles? Would not his normal cousins have won out, survived, and passed on uricase to the anthropoids and men of today.

The answer is, yes. That is, yes, unless the absence of uricase had survival value that made up for the disadvantages.—And here comes a piece of speculation I encountered recently in a chemical-news weekly.

The absence of uricase means that the concentration of uric acid in the blood and tissues of apes and man is higher than in that of other species. Uric acid is a member of a group of compounds called purines, some members of which are stimulants of the nervous system. The purine stimulant you are probably best acquainted with is the caffeine in coffee. Now what if a higher concentration of uric acid in the blood of the pre-anthropoid who lost uricase kept him at a higher level of mental activity than was the case with his uricase-containing cousins. Would not that have more than made up for the off-chance possibility of gout? Could not the uric acid, in fact, have been one of the chemical factors involved in stimulating gradual development of the brain into the large specialized structures now present in apes and, particularly, in man. If so, what price gout?

Consider the manner in which life-forms moved out of the sea (in which life originated) into fresh water and onto land. That involved not only the familiar morphological evolution, but biochemical evolution as well. In the sea, cells developed in a liquid containing certain ions (chiefly sodium, potassium, calcium, magnesium, chloride and sulfate ions) in certain concentrations.

Life made the adjustment to those concentrations once and apparently that was it for all time.

When animals grew more complicated and became a group of cells enclosed in some form of shell, skin, protective membrane or what have you, the individual cells remained immersed in an inner liquid resembling sea water in ionic composition. The outer portions of the body, as well as many other things, changed to suit altered conditions when animals moved out onto the land, but the internal liquid, the liquid with which the cells were in actual contact, remained about the same. Our own blood, after you subtract the various blood cells and dissolved proteins and other organic material, is remarkably like a quantity of trapped sea water, and so is the interstitial fluid that exists in the spaces between our cells.

In other words, we've never left the sea; we've taken it with us.

(To be sure the resemblance between the ionic composition of blood and sea-water is not exact. Some people suggest that our blood resembles the primeval sea; the sea as it was when organisms first enclosed themselves; and that since then, the ocean has changed its composition somewhat, this change not being reflected in our blood.)

This may seem to you as though biochemical evolution is something that does *not* happen, but remember the Red Queen's advice that in her country it takes all the running one can do to stay in one place.

Primitive sea creatures have no trouble maintaining the ionic composition of their internal fluids because it is mostly in even balance with sea water, and they have learned, with the millions of years, to tolerate slight changes that may develop in sea water and hence in their own fluids. But when a sea creature invades the fresh water (which, biochemically, is as difficult a feat as the invasion of land) a completely new situation develops.

Fresh water is only a thousandth as rich in ions as is sea water. When a sea creature tries to live in fresh water, it must somehow counteract the natural tendency of the ions within itself to leak out (or, for that matter, for water to leak in) and equalize the ionic concentration inside and outside the animal.

To do that, fresh-water animals have developed a number of intricate biochemical mechanisms to keep the ion composition of their internal liquid steady at the values to which they are accustomed. They have evolved, biochemically, like mad just to stay in the same place.

In one way or another, the mechanisms usually involve kidney action. Water is constantly entering the fresh-water creature, and ions enter, too, by way of the food it eats. The kidneys are so designed that they pass water out again but hold back the ions. The creature is thus an ion-trapping sieve.

It is considered that any creature that can keep a surplus of ions inside its body against a deficiency on the outside must have had some ancestor that adapted itself to fresh-water. All vertebrates apparently come into this classification and so it is deduced biochemically that the original vertebrate from which all others are descended developed in fresh-water.

To be sure, a number of fresh-water vertebrates migrated back to the sea, to become the ancestors of the marine fish and marine sharks (the two are not the same, the fish being bony and more advanced, the sharks cartilaginous and more primitive) of today. By the time the fish and sharks returned to the sea, the sea-water was a bit richer in ions than their internal liquid was. They had the reverse problem now; to keep surplus ions from entering or (which amounts to the same thing) water from leaving. The fish solved the problem by cutting down on water loss through kidneys and by evolving special biochemical mechanisms to force ions out. (The sharks had another solution, which I'll mention later.)

You can find details, by the way, of this and other similar matters in an excellent little book by Ernest Baldwin called *Comparative Biochemistry*, published by the Cambridge University Press in 1948.

The conquest of the dry land involved a whole new series of biochemical modifications. One of these concerned the matter of waste-disposal.

The chief elements found in the organic materials of living creatures are carbon, hydrogen, oxygen, and nitrogen (which chemists symbolize as C, H, O, and N respectively). When foodstuffs (which include complicated molecules built up out of anywhere from dozens to millions of atoms of these elements, plus a few others) are broken down for energy, what is left behind are simple molecules which are waste-products to be eliminated. The carbon, hydrogen and oxygen end up as carbon dioxide (CO_2) and water (H_2O). In the case of most water-dwelling animals, the nitrogen ends up as ammonia (NH_3).

Now for any creature living in fresh water, there is no problem. Carbon dioxide and ammonia are soluble in water, and water is just water. Dump all three substances into the river. The waste water will just mix with the river-water, the carbon dioxide will come in handy to the water plants, the ammonia will eventually be utilized by plants and bacteria. The plants and bacteria will build carbon dioxide, water, and ammonia back into the complicated molecules that the animals will again swallow, digest, and use for energy and to build their own tissues. Round and round things go.

In fact, the only suspicion of risk involves ammonia which is highly poisonous. One part in 20,000 in blood is enough to kill. Fortunately for the fresh water fish, they're passing so much water through their kidneys in their effort to keep up their ion content that the ammonia is flushed out as fast as it is formed and never has the chance to build up even the small concentration needed for poisoning.

What about sea-fish which pass less water through their kidneys? They still manage to flush out the ammonia adequately, though in their case it's much more of a near squeak.

But then we reach the amphibia (toads, frogs, etc.), the first vertebrates to invade the land. As water-dwelling tadpoles, they excrete ammonia, but as adult, land-living creatures, ammonia is no longer possible. Water is in such short supply for any creature that doesn't live actually immersed in it, that it can't possibly be spent sufficiently recklessly to keep the ammonia concentration low enough.

Before any creature could invade the land, then, it had to develop a type of nitrogen waste that was considerably less poisonous than ammonia. The adult amphibian accomplished this. It broke its nitrogen down to urea (NH_2–CO–NH_2). As you see, the urea molecule is made up of a fusion of the parts of two ammonia molecules and one carbon dioxide molecule. Urea is soluble in water and is much less poisonous than ammonia. It can be allowed to build up to a much higher concentration than ammonia so that a given amount of nitrogen waste can be eliminated in a much smaller quantity of urine, and precious water is conserved.

Here we have one case where a biochemical invention was made independently more than once. The sharks (who preceded the amphibia and were not ancestral to them), after migrating from their fresh-water origin back to the sea were faced with keeping ions from the ocean surplus from invading their body. Instead of developing ion-excreting mechanisms as the marine fish did, they worked out the trick of breaking down nitrogen compounds to urea instead of ammonia. Then they allowed urea to concentrate in the blood as they could never have done with ammonia.

In fact, they allowed urea to accumulate to a concentration of 2 per cent, which is enough to kill other creatures. (Even though urea is less poisonous than ammonia, it isn't entirely harmless. Nothing is.) Through the ages, shark tissue acclimated itself to urea. The urea in the blood acted as the ions did, in a way, and made the total ion content (with urea included) of shark blood higher than that of the ocean. The problem was therefore once again to keep the ions from leaking out and the sharks could use their old fresh-water adaptations for the purpose instead of having to invent new mechanisms, as the sea fish did.

So you see, although sharks and amphibia developed the same urea dodge independently, they did so for different reasons.

Incidentally, some sharks migrated back to fresh water after having developed the urea-waste mechanism. Once in fresh water, the presence of urea in the blood was not only unnecessary, it was down right embarrassing. It made the ion content of the blood artificially high so that it was harder than ever to keep it steady against the ion-free fresh water. The fresh-water sharks did the best they could by cutting down the urea concentration in blood from 2 per cent to 0·6 per cent, but there they reached their limit. Shark tissue had grown so accustomed to urea, it had become positively dependent upon it. Shark heart, for instance, won't beat in blood containing no urea. (Our hearts would do fine.) So you see, biochemistry can be a tricky thing.

Even urea requires a certain amount of water to be eliminated. It's all right for frogs and toads. One way or another they get enough water, even those species that seem to live away from water, and their eggs are always supplied with plenty of water.

Of the vertebrates descended from amphibia, the mammals, too, produce urea. They get ample water for the purpose and their young develop viviparously, that is, within the mother's body, where it is always in contact with the mother's water supply.

The birds and reptiles are another case completely. They lay eggs and within those eggs, the young must develop. The chick egg, for instance, can contain only a certain amount of water and for the three weeks between fertilization and hatching, the young chick must make that do because it will not get one drop more.

Water-economy becomes more important than ever. There isn't even enough water to take care of urea, so urea becomes inadequate as a waste product. A new invention is necessary. That new invention is uric acid (which I mentioned earlier). Uric acid contains the fragments of four ammonia molecules and three carbon dioxide molecules, and its advantage over urea is this: uric acid is quite insoluble in water. (Remember, that is its *disadvantage* in man.) The young bird or reptile developing in the egg just piles up the uric acid wastes in a little dump heap. Little or no water is required.

As is well known, morphological evolution can be traced in

embryos. At various times during development, a human embryo passes through a unicellular stage, an invertebrate stage, and a cartilaginous stage. It shows at various times gills, a tail and a pelt of body hair. In the same way, biochemical evolution can be traced.

The developing chick excretes mostly ammonia for the first four days, when the total excretion is so small and the egg so large in comparison to the tiny embryo that dangerous concentrations are not reached. Then for the next nine days, nitrogen wastes are mostly in the form of urea, there still being a reasonable amount of water to keep the urea concentration low enough. Finally, during the last eleven days when things are getting tight, the wastes are mostly in the form of uric acid.

Turtles seem to be betwixt and between. Their egg-laying is done in closer contact with seas or rivers and they apparently produce both urea and uric acid.

Again a duplication of inventions. Certain invertebrates have also invaded the land (some even earlier than ever the vertebrates did). The insects and land-snails, for instance, also invented the uric acid dodge, quite independently.

I have already mentioned the fact that from biochemical considerations we can say that vertebrates first developed in fresh water. It is also possible to speculate from other biochemical considerations about the ancestry of the vertebrates.

It seems, you see, that there is an important compound in our muscles which is intimately connected with the mechanism whereby muscles contract and relax. It is called creatine phosphate and we will abbreviate it as CP. Now here's an interesting thing: CP is found in vertebrate muscle of all sorts, but it is *not* found in invertebrate muscle.

Invertebrate muscle contains instead a similar compound with similar functions, called arginine phosphate, which we can abbreviate as AP.

Now the problem is: at what point in evolution was CP invented as a substitute for AP. Since all vertebrates have CP, it was probably invented at some point before the vertebrate developed (unless the different groups of vertebrates each invented it independently, which seems unlikely).

Well, the vertebrates (which are characterized by bony skeletons) are part of a larger group of animals called the chordata. The less advanced animals in this group haven't reached the point where they have bones, but instead have inner stiffenings of some softer material. The indispensable minimum that makes an animal a member of the chordata is the presence of a cartilaginous rod called a notochord inside the body at some time in life.

There are three groups of these primitive chordates. The most advanced type is amphioxus, which is fish-shaped (with fins missing and a fringed hole where a mouth and jaws should be). It has a notochord running the length of its body all the days of its life. Its muscles have CP, just as your muscles do.

The most primitive of these primitives are the tunicates, which show a small scrap of notochord in their larval form. As adults, they lose it altogether and are so invertebrate in appearance that they were originally classified as molluscs. The tunicates have AP in their muscles, just as invertebrates do.

The intermediate group of the three includes the balanoglossus, a worm-like creature. It doesn't have a fully developed notochord, but it does have a scrap of it that hangs on into adult life.

Well, to end the suspense, balanoglossus muscle has both AP and CP.

Can CP be traced further back?

The answer is yes. The larvae of balanoglossus resemble the larvae of certain echinoderms (a group of animals that includes the familiar starfish) so much that before the adult form of the balanoglossus was discovered, the larvae were classified as echinoderms.

What about the echinoderms, then? These are divided into a number of groups, of which the majority, including the starfish, contain AP in their muscles just as other invertebrates do. However, there is one group, the brittle stars (which resemble star fish except that the 'arms' are longer and more flexible, and emerge from a globular little 'body') with muscles that contain CP, as do those of vertebrates. The final group, the sea-urchins (with spiny bodies shaped like discs that are round above and flat below) contain both CP and AP.

CP can't be traced any further back, so far. It would seem then that at some time in the past, some creature (of which the sea-urchin is the most direct descendant) invented CP.

So if you should ever see a sea-urchin, be respectful. Of all the invertebrates from amebae to insects and from worms to octopi, it is possibly your closest relative.

CHAPTER TEN

THE SOUND OF PANTING

B ACK in September of 1950, Dr. William C. Boyd, Professor of Immunochemistry at Boston University School
of Medicine—where I work—having just come back from
several months in Egypt, and feeling full of spirit, lured me
to one side and suggested that we write a textbook on biochemistry for medical students. This struck me as a terrific idea.
Dr. Boyd had already written textbooks on blood-grouping, on
immunology and on anthropology, so there was no doubt in
my mind that he could supply the experience. As for myself I
felt I could supply the enthusiasm. We then rung in Dr.
Burnham S. Walker, who is the head of our department of biochemistry and who has an encyclopedic knowledge of the subject. He went along not only with the notion but also with
alacrity.

There followed a hectic interval in which we laid our plans,
corralled a publisher and had a lot of fun. But there came a time
when all the preliminaries were over and we came face to face
with a typewriter and a clean sheet of paper.

It took us a year and a half before the first edition was done
and additional years to produce new editions. The title of the
book is *Biochemistry and Human Metabolism* (Williams and
Wilkins) and the third edition appeared in the autumn of 1957.
As all this went on I learned a lot about textbooks.

A textbook, after all, is an orderly presentation of what is
known in a given branch of science and is intended to be used
for the instruction of students. Note the word 'orderly'. It
implies that a textbook must begin at the beginning, proceed
through the various stages of the middle, and end at the end.
Unfortunately, unless the science concerned is a deductive one
such as mathematics or logic, this neat procedure is hampered
by the fact that there is no beginning, no middle and no end.

An inductive science such as biochemistry consists, essentially, of a vast agglomeration of data out of which a number of

thinkers have abstracted certain tentative conclusions. It resembles a three-dimensional lacework all knotted together. To expound any portion of biochemistry properly, a certain knowledge of other areas of the science must be assumed. It is, therefore, the task of the writer to decide what one-dimensional order of presentation is least confusing. What subjects can he discuss in the earlier chapters with the best chance of being understood despite the absence of information contained in the later chapters? How often must an author stop to explain at a given point and how often can he get away with a simple reference to a page halfway up the book, or even with a curt 'See Appendix'? (I, by the way, was a devotee of the 'stop and explain' method and I was consequently periodically crushed by the democratic procedure of being outvoted two to one.)

Note also that a textbook is intended to instruct students. This cannot be done by lulling them gently to sleep or by confusing them with a display of incomprehensible brilliance. As far as is consistent with a respect for the facts and for accurate exposition, one must not scorn to write entertainingly. In short, there is the question of style.

This raises the point that three collaborators have three different styles. True! Fortunately, by dint of revising each other's work and then beating out the results in triple conference, a reasonably uniform style was achieved with elimination of extremes. Dr. Walker, for instance, whose natural style is extremely condensed, was forced to include occasional conjunctions and to allow the existence of a few subordinate clauses. I, on the other hand, found that my more passionate outbursts of lyricism were ruthlessly pruned. Many was the gallant rearguard fight by one or another of us in an attempt to insert a comma or delete it; many the anguished search through the Unabridged in defense of a maligned word.

However, back to my definition of textbook. It is an orderly presentation of *what is known*. The implication is that it deals with what is known up to the very moment of writing.

That's easy, isn't it?

And how does one find out what is known?

First of all, there are other textbooks, and one naturally turns to them for another man's panoramic view of a field. But there are limitations to the textbook.

For instance, textbooks must be selective, rather than inclusive, as that is the only chance of staying below ten thousand pages. This means that the author of the textbook you read has already winnowed the facts and his winnowing may not be your notion of winnowing at all. Secondly, every textbook writer imposes his own interpretation on the data, either by actually stating his interpretation, or by implying it through his choice of what facts to place in the book.

(Occasionally, we three co-authors didn't agree on interpretations among ourselves. For instance, there are two major theories concerning the cause of cancer. One is the 'mutation theory' and one is the 'virus theory'. I'm a mutation fan and Dr. Boyd is a virus supporter. Since I had the cancer chapter in my charge in editions one and two, I pitched mutation into a page or two of eloquent prose and dismissed viruses in a cool, unimpassioned paragraph. Such arguments! Scarcely a lunch hour passed in which Dr. Boyd didn't advance determinedly to the fight, armed with a new article on the virus theory. He has managed to win me over somewhat and in the next edition of the book, I think he will be in charge of the cancer chapter.)

Probing more deeply than the textbook, we come to the monograph. The monograph is no attempt at instructing beginners at all. It is a presentation of *all* the available facts—within human limitations—for the benefit of the expert in the field. The subject of the monograph is, of necessity, narrower—and usually much narrower—than the subject of the textbook.

The one-man monograph is vanishing. That is the result, in part, of the growing ocean of known fact and the consequent narrowing of focus of the human mind. The 'universal genius' is gone forever. Nowadays, it is almost impossible to find a man who considers himself qualified to write all about some small subdivision of biochemistry, which is itself a subdivision of biology and chemistry, which are themselves subdivisions of the field of the physical sciences which are themselves subdivisions——

Take an example. Recently an extensive monograph on proteins has been coming out. It is in four volumes—total pages, 2,526; total price $54.00. It is edited by two men, but it contains a series of articles to which a total of thirty-one authors have contributed, one of them being Dr. Boyd, incidentally. Each chapter is a 'review article' concerning some subdivision of the biochemistry of proteins.

Scientists are very grateful for review articles. They summarize the 'literature' (I'll explain what that means in a little while) in one finely-focused facet of the science.

Whole systems of volumes are devoted to nothing but review articles. For instance, every year for the last twenty-odd, a book called *Annual Reviews of Biochemistry* has come out. It is divided into chapters, each dealing with a subdivision of biochemistry and each written by an appropriate expert. Each chapter summarizes the work that has been done in that subdivision over the past year as concisely as possible. Despite the fact that the book is concise almost to the point of obscurity, it ends by being a good-sized volume.

Then there are periodicals like *Chemical Reviews* and *Physiological Reviews*, which don't try to cover the whole field every issue. They appear at monthly intervals with selected reviews on this subject or that. The July, 1954 issue of *Physiological Reviews*, for instance, has eight reviews, including a twenty-five-page article on the single substance, serotonin, a compound of importance in the workings of the brain which was first identified in 1949. The August, 1954 issue of *Chemical Reviews* contains four review articles, including twenty-four pages on the microheterogeneity of proteins (a subject bearing on my discourse in Chapter 3).

Annual volumes are also put out containing review articles on more restricted subject matter. For instance *Advances in Enzymology* was first put out in 1940 and has been appearing annually since. It contains review articles dealing only with enzymes and related subjects. This sort of specialized review volume proved so useful and desirable that other subdivisions of biochemistry demanded similar service.

A single publishing house now puts out *Advances in Protein Chemistry*, *Advances in Carbohydrate Chemistry*, *Advances in Cancer Research*, *Advances in Genetics*, *Advances in Virus Research*, *Advances in Food Research*, *Advances in Agronomy*,

Vitamins and Hormones, Recent Progress in Hormone Research, International Review of Cytology, Progress in Biophysics and Biophysical Interactions, Progress in Organic Chemistry, The Alkaloids. Each appears once a year or so, and there are many others to keep these company.

But all these, textbooks, monographs, reviews, are only secondary sources. Where do they get their information?

Well, the primary source of knowledge is derived from all the work done in all the laboratories, libraries, offices and thinking places, of all the colleges, universities, research institutions, industrial establishments, hospitals and similar places by all the scientists, engineers, physicians and technicians.

Whenever any of these has completed a series of experiments or arrived at a certain set of thoughts which seem to yield a small nugget of useful information which does not completely coincide with any of the other nuggets of useful information of which he is aware, it is his bounden duty to make known this nugget to the scientific world.

This is done by writing a 'paper'; that is, by preparing a description of his experiments and their results, preceded by a very brief summary of previous work in the field and succeeded by a cautious interpretation of the significance of his own work. The paper is then submitted for publication in a periodical devoted to such things. Such periodicals are referred to, in rather cavalier fashion, as 'journals' and the sum total of all the papers written is referred to, still more cavalierly, as the 'literature'. (I told you we'd get around to that word.)

There are literally thousands of journals printed. I'll confine myself to journals of biochemistry and we'll run through a couple, just to get the taste of things. The aristocrat of biochemical journals is the *Journal of Biological Chemistry*. It comes out once a month and the individual issues have been thickening with the years. When it first appeared some fifty years ago, the entire year's output could be bound into a moderately sized volume. The year's output is now bound into six somewhat larger volumes. The British analogue is the *Biochemical Journal*, which has fewer but larger pages.

There is the *Journal of the American Chemical Society*, which specializes in physical chemistry and organic chemistry, although the biochemical papers it contains are first rate. It comes out twice a month now—the monthly issue became too unwieldy. The British analogue is the *Journal of the Chemical Society*.

There is *Science*, which appears weekly and specializes in short papers covering the entire field of the sciences, with biochemistry well represented. The British analogue is *Nature*.

We haven't even scraped the surface, though. There are journals devoted to specific diseases, with titles like *Cancer*, *Cancer Research*, *Diabetes* and so on. There are journals devoted to particular parts of the body or particular aspects of its mechanism, like *Blood*, *Circulation*, *Brain*, *Metabolism*. There are journals put out by various scientific institutes or organizations, such as: *Proceedings of the Society for Experimental Biology and Medicine*, *Proceedings of the National Academy of Sciences of the United States*, *Journal of the National Cancer Institute*, *Annals of the New York Academy of Science*, *Bulletin of the New York Academy of Medicine*. There are journals devoted to certain branches of biochemistry or to allied subjects: *Journal of Immunology*, *Journal of Bacteriology*, *Journal of Nutrition*, *Journal of Clinical Nutrition*, *Journal of Clinical Investigation*, *American Journal of Clinical Pathology*, *Journal of Clinical Endocrinology*. (I'm just pulling them out of the air at random.) Various schools and hospitals put out journals devoted to their own work: There is the *Quarterly Bulletin of Northwestern University Medical School*, *Yale Journal of Biology and Medicine*, and many more.

Furthermore, new journals are continually being brought into existence. Just this week, I received the announcement of a new journal, *Virology*, to come out approximately bimonthly and to be devoted to the various aspects of virus research.

And then, you know, science is international. There are whole clusters of foreign-language journals. The Germans have *Zeitschrift für Physiologische Chemie* as their chief biochemical journal. The French have *Comptes rendus des séances de la societé de biologie et de ses filiales* as theirs. The Russians, of course, have moved up in journal production in recent years, and if you want to see what the title of a Russian journal looks like—transliterated from the Cyrillic alphabet—try this on for size: *Doklady Akademii Nauk Soyuza Sovetskikh Sotsialisticheskikh Respublik*—which means 'Proceedings of the Academy of Sciences of the Union of Soviet Socialist Republics'. There are Japanese journals, Swedish journals, Swiss journals, Dutch journals, Spanish and various Latin-American journals. There's the *Journal of the Pharmaceutical Association of Siam*, *Journal of the Philippine Medical Association*, *The Irish Journal of Medical Science* and so on and so on and so on——

(Special note: I am not making up a thing. Every journal listed in this article is a real, honest for true, genuine journal.)

Now, then, the number of papers of biochemical interest which appear in these journals amounts to some twenty-five hundred *each month*. How does any biochemist keep up with them? Reading them all is out of the question. Yet unless we get acquainted somehow with all of them, how can we tell but what some extremely vital nugget of information is escaping us?

(You think such escape isn't possible? When Mendel discovered the basic laws of genetics, he duly published his results in the *Proceedings of the Natural History Society of Brünn*, where it lay quietly undisturbed and unnoticed for thirty-four years. Count 'em. Thirty-four.)

And biochemists make an effort to 'keep up with the literature'. Every paper lists a dozen or so other papers in the field. Every review article lists a hundred to a thousand. For instance, the article on serotonin which I mentioned earlier in the paper includes a listing of one hundred and fifty-seven papers, or 'references' as they are called. The one on microheterogeneity of proteins includes one hundred and sixty-four references.

But where do writers of papers and, particularly, of review articles get their lists of references? Fortunately, there are journals which devote themselves to nothing more than preparing 'abstracts' of scientific papers. That is, with the aid of an army of technically trained people willing to work for the good of science and a nominal sum, the journal will try to keep track of every paper appearing in every journal related to their field. They will list for every paper all over the world, the title, author or authors, name, volume, month or page of the journal, and a short summary of the paper's contents. The most important such journal for our purposes is *Chemical Abstracts*, which abstracts all foreign papers in the very best English.

Chemical Abstracts comes out twice a month. An individual issue has up to four hundred large pages in double columns and microscopic print. Each column is numbered separately beginning with the first issue of a year and ending with the last. The total number of columns per year—of the listing of papers only—used to reach eight thousand ten years ago. It now reaches seventeen thousand.

Every year *Chemical Abstracts* publishes an extensive and exhaustive author index and subject index. They come out in three volumes and add up to more than a thousand pages. When I first became interested in such things, the index came out three months after the year ended. As it has grown larger, longer, and more complicated, it comes out now nearly a year after the year ended. This means that there is always a minimum of say twenty issues and a maximum of forty issues of *Chemical Abstracts* unindexed. These unindexed issues are the latest ones which contain the latest papers.

This means that if you're trying to read up on the work done in a given field, you first exhaust the indices for the last ten years, say, then get grimly to work on the individual issues of the last year or two.

And when you've got the entire field of biochemistry to keep up with for the sake of a textbook—ouch, each aching vertebra.

Review articles are a boon and a gift from the gods, but even one which is freshly printed and which contains the latest information, can't include all the papers in the field or do more than refer very cursorily to most of those it does include. It never hurts to do a little browsing through *Chemical Abstracts* on your own, which, by the way, lists all review articles. Furthermore, the number of review articles being published now is so great, that you can't read all you should of those either.

In preparing future editions of the text, the one great problem is 'bringing it up to date' and for that *Chemical Abstracts* is absolutely necessary. My own method is to grab Dr. Walker's issue of *Chemical Abstracts* (he subscribes!) as soon as it comes in, preferably before Dr. Walker gets his hooks on them. Fortunately, *Chemical Abstracts* segregates its paper listings into over twenty subdivisions of chemistry and I can ignore sections dealing with industrial chemicals, paper and paper-making chemicals, electrochemistry, photography and so on. Unfortunately, the listings under Biochemistry—itself subdivided into ten sub-subdivisions—is the longest in the periodical.

I cuddle up with one hundred to one hundred and fifty large pages containing one thousand to one thousand five hundred articles twice a month, in other words, and read dizzily through the titles. Sometimes a title is short, like 'Iron Metabolism' which usually indicates a review. (All reviews are automatically noted down by me provided they are in a journal I can obtain. In one place or another in Boston I can obtain almost all the unimportant journals and all the important ones. I can obtain almost all the important ones by going to the school library two floors below my lab.)

Sometimes the title is long, like for instance: *Use of Ion Exchangers for the Separation of some of the Amino Acids formed during the Enzymic Degradation of Cysteinesulfinic Acid. Application to the Isolation of Hypotaurine (2-Aminoethanesulfinic Acid)*, which is the real title of a real paper. Long titles like this are fashionable not because scientists are queer, but because a good title is one which will give you a complete idea of the contents of the paper, without your having to read anything further. That's not laziness on our part, friend, that's one of our barriers against insanity.

If a title of a paper is interesting, I read the abstract itself. If the abstract looks interesting, I note the volume of *Chemical Abstracts*, the number of its column and its position in that column in a special volume of our textbook with a blank page between every two printed pages. I make the entry opposite the place in the book where I think it belongs.

The results? Well, they can be harrowing. Take the case of the function of the metal, molybdenum, in the human body. In the first edition of our book, it wasn't even worth mentioning and we didn't mention it. By the time we wrote the second edition, some workers had showed it to be a constituent of an important enzyme known as xanthine dehydrogenase. We stuck in molybdenum, therefore, and gave it seven lines. By the time the third edition rolled round there were thirty new papers to be read, or at the very least, glanced through, in order that we might increase the space devoted to molybdenum from seven lines to two paragraphs, and do it intelligently. And this despite pruning the number ruthlessly by first picking only those with interesting titles and, of those, only the ones with interesting-sounding abstracts.

And this isn't really enough, you know. Even *Chemical Abstracts* isn't up to date. They're anywhere from six months to a year behind the journals. One ought, therefore, to glance at the titles in the most important journals as they come out. But then, the journals aren't up to date, either. A paper which is accepted for publication by the *Journal of Biological Chemistry* may have to wait six months to a year before seeing the light. The journal has that great a backlog of accepted papers. Besides that, a paper deals with work that is completed. There is other, newer work in progress.

And so there are all sorts of conventions. The American Chemical Society holds annual conventions in various parts of the country. The Federation of American Societies for Experimental Biology—which includes six subsidiary societies— holds annual conventions. So does the American Association for the Advancement of Science. So do innumerable smaller groups. At each one of these, papers are presented. Hundreds of papers are presented at the largest gatherings, where several subgroups are usually giving series of papers simultaneously in different rooms of the hotel—sometimes in different hotels and sometimes even in different cities. It is impossible for one man to hear more than a fraction of these and he must choose his spots with care and hope for the best.

Of the three of us, Dr. Boyd is the most indefatigable attender of conventions. In recent months, he has been to New York, Philadelphia, French Lick (Indiana) and Paris (France) in order to give papers, listen to papers and—most important of all—get together over a glass of beer and find out what's doing in the other guy's lab right at that moment.

And so it goes.

There is now a whole branch of human effort devoted to attempts to coördinate the accumulating data of the physical sciences at a rate roughly equivalent to that at which it is accumulating. This includes the formulation of special types of indices and codes, the use of screening programs, the preparation of special punched cards, micro-card files and so on.

In connection with this, I should like to quote a passage from a letter written by Karl F. Heumann, Director of the Chemical-Biological Coördination Center of the National Research Council to Mr. Ken Deveney, Jr., of Millington, New Jersey. A carbon copy was sent to John Campbell, the editor of *Astounding Science Fiction*, who forwarded it to me. The passage reads:

Dear Dr. Deveney:

In answer to your question ... about data-handling, I would like to give you a short bibliography but it is not possible. There has been a great increase in work in this field which has resulted in a scattering of documentation references among various abstracting services. ...

In other words, the literature relating to efforts to handle the literature is too great to be handled easily.

Get it?

There's no way out and each year it's getting worse.

—And so, if you are ever up Boston way, and enter the Boston University School of Medicine and pass my lab and hear the sound of panting, you may think it is the result of my chasing some female around and around some desk—but you'd be wrong.

It's just Asimov trying to keep up with the literature, a task which is much more futile and far less likely to reach a satisfactory conclusion.

SPECIAL NOTE

The two chapters that follow, unlike the preceding, are *not* legitimate reporting and speculation. Rather they are a gentle spoofing of science and scientific papers.

In the case of each, one outrageous assumption is made, so that we are presented with a most unusual chemical compound in the first and an equally unusual bird in the second. Once this assumption is made, everything else follows more or less plausibly. Don't let this plausibility fool you, however, into taking either article seriously.

CHAPTER ELEVEN

THE MARVELLOUS PROPERTIES OF THIOTIMOLINE

PART I

THE correlation of the structure of organic molecules with their various properties, physical and chemical, has in recent years afforded much insight into the mechanism of organic reactions, notably in the theories of resonance and mesomerism. The solubilities of organic compounds in various solvents has become of particular interest in this connection through the recent discovery of the endochronic nature of thiotimoline.[1]

It has been long known that the solubility of organic compounds in polar solvents such as water is enhanced by the presence upon the hydrocarbon nucleus of hydrophilic—i.e. water-loving—groups, such as the hydroxy (–OH), amino (–NH_2), or sulfonic acid (–SO_3H) groups. Where the physical characteristics of two given compounds—particularly the degree of subdivision of the material—are equal, then the time of solution—expressed in seconds per gram of material per milliliter of solvent—decreases with the number of hydrophilic groups present. Catechol, for instance, with two hydroxy groups on the benzene nucleus dissolves considerably more quickly than does phenol with only one hydroxy group on the nucleus. Feinschreiber and Hravlek[2] in their studies on the problem have contended that with increasing hydrophilism, the time of solution approaches zero. That this analysis is not entirely correct was shown when it was discovered that the compound thiotimoline will dissolve in water—in the proportions of 1 gm. /ml.—in *minus* 1·12 seconds. That is, it will dissolve *before* the water is added.

Previous communications from these laboratories indicated thiotimoline to contain at least fourteen hydroxy groups, two amino groups and one sulfonic acid group.[3] The presence of a nitro group (–NO_2) in addition has not yet been confirmed and no evidence as yet exists as to the nature of the hydrocarbon nucleus, though an at least partly aromatic structure seems certain.

The Endochronometer—First attempts to measure the time of solution of thiotimoline quantitatively met with considerable difficulty because of the very negative nature of the value. The fact that the chemical dissolved prior to the addition of the water made the attempt natural to withdraw the water after solution and before addition. This, fortunately for the law of Conservation of Mass-Energy, never succeeded since solution never took place unless the water was eventually added. The question is, of course, instantly raised as to how the thiotimoline can 'know' in advance whether the water will ultimately be added or not. Though this is not properly within our province as physical chemists, much recent material has been published within the last year upon the psychological and philosophical problems thereby posed.[4, 5]

Nevertheless, the chemical difficulties involved rest in the fact that the time of solution varies enormously with the exact mental state of the experimenter. A period of even slight hesitation in adding the water reduces the negative time of solution, not infrequently wiping it out below the limits of detection. To avoid this, a mechanical device has been constructed, the essential design of which has already been reported in a previous communication.[6] This device, termed the endochronometer, consists of a cell 2 cubic centimeters in size into which a desired weight of thiotimoline is placed, making certain that a small hollow extension at the bottom of the solution cell—1 millimeter in internal diameter—is filled. To the cell, is attached an automatic pressure micro-pipette containing a specific volume of the solvent concerned. Five seconds after the circuit is closed, this solvent is automatically delivered into the cell containing the thiotimoline. During the time of action, a ray of light is focused upon the small cell-extension described above, and at the instant of solution, the transmission of this light will no longer be impeded by the presence of solid thiotimoline. Both the instant of solution—at which time the transmission of light is recorded by a photoelectric device—and the instant of solvent addition can be determined with an accuracy of better than 0·01 per cent. If the first value is subtracted from the second, the time of solution (T) can be determined.

The entire process is conducted in a theromstat maintained at 25·00° C.—to an accuracy of 0·01° C.

Thiotimoline Purity—The extreme sensitivity of this method highlights the deviations resulting from trifling impurities present in thiotimoline. (Since no method of laboratory synthesis of the substance has been devised, it may be practically obtained only through tedious isolation from its natural source, the bark of the shrub *Rosacea Karlsbadensis rufo.*[7]) Great efforts were therefore made to purify the material through repeated recrystallizations from conductivity water—twice re-distilled in an all-tin apparatus—and through final sublimations. A comparison of the solution times (T) at various stages of the purification process is shown in Table I.

TABLE I

Purification Stage	Average 'T' (12 observations)	'T' extremes	% error
As Isolated	−0·72	−0·25; −1·01	34·1
First recrystallization	−0·95	−0·84; −1·09	9·8
Second recrystallization	−1·05	−0·99; −1·10	4·0
Third recrystallization	−1·11	−1·08; −1·13	1·8
Fourth recrystallization	−1·12	−1·10; −1·13	1·7
First resublimation	−1·12	−1·11; −1·13	0·9
Second resublimation	−1·122	−1·12; −1·13	0·7

It is obvious from Table I that for truly quantitative significance, thiotimoline purified as described must be used. After the second resublimation, for instance, the error involved in an even dozen determinations is less than 0·7 per cent with the extreme values being −1·119 seconds and −1·126 seconds.

In all experiments described subsequently in this study, thiotimoline so purified has been used.

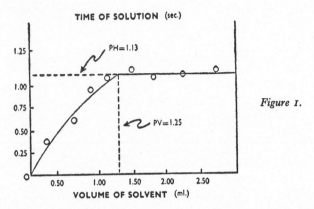

Figure 1.

Time of Solution and Volume of Solvent—As would seem reasonable, experiments have shown that increasing the volume of solvent enables the thiotimoline to dissolve more quickly—*i.e.* with an increasingly negative time of solution. From Figure 1, however, we can see that this increase in endochronic properties levels off rapidly after a volume of solvent of approximately 1·25 ml. This interesting plateau effect has appeared with varying volume of solvent for all varieties of solvents used in these laboratories, just as in all cases the time of solution approaches zero with decreasing volume of solvent.

Time of Solution and Concentration of a Given Ion—In Figure 2, the results are given of the effect of the time of

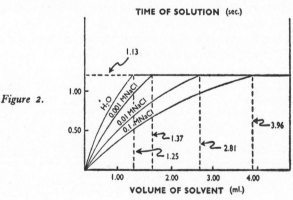

Figure 2.

solution (T) of varying the volume of solvent, where the solvent consists of varying concentrations of sodium chloride solution. It can be seen that although in each case, the volume at which this plateau is reached differs markedly with the concentration, the heights of the plateau are constant (*i.e.* $-1\cdot13$). The volume at which it is reached, hereinafter termed the Plateau Volume (PV), decreases with decreasing concentration of sodium chloride, approaching the PV for water as the NaCl concentration approaches zero. It is, therefore, obvious that a sodium chloride solution of unknown concentration can be quite accurately characterized by the determination of its PV, where other salts are absent.

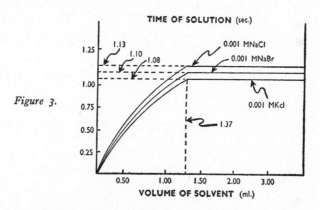

Figure 3.

This usefulness of PV extends to other ions as well. Figure 3 gives the endochronic curves for $0\cdot001$ molar solutions of sodium chloride, sodium bromide, and potassium chloride. Here, the PV in each case is equal within the limits of experimental error—since the concentrations in each case are equal— but the Plateau Heights (PH) *are* different.

A tentative conclusion that might be reached from this experimental data is that the PH is characteristic of the nature of the ions present in solution whereas the PV is characteristic of the concentration of these ions. Table II gives the values of Plateau Height and Plateau Volume for a wide variety of salts in equal concentrations, when present alone.

The most interesting variation to be noted in Table II is

TABLE II

Solvent (*Salt solutions in* 0·001 *M concentration*)	*Plateau Height* (PH) *seconds*	*Plateau Volume* (PV) *milliliters*
Water	−1·13	1·25
Sodium Chloride solution	−1·13	1·37
Sodium Bromide solution	−1·10	1·37
Potassium Chloride solution	−1·08	1·37
Sodium Sulphate solution	−0·72	1·59
Calcium Chloride solution	−0·96	1·58
Magnesium Chloride solution	−0·85	1·59
Calcium Sulphate solution	−0·61	1·72
Sodium Phosphate solution	−0·32	1·97
Ferric Chloride solution	−0·29	1·99

that of the PV with the valence type of the salt present. In the case of salts containing pairs of singly-charged ions—*i.e.* sodium chloride, potassium chloride, and sodium bromide— the PV is constant for all. This holds also for those salts containing one singly charged ion and one doubly charged ion—*i.e.* sodium sulphate, calcium chloride, and magnesium chloride— where the PV, though equal among the three varies markedly from those of the first set. The PV is, therefore, apparently a function of the ionic strength of the solution.

This effect also exists in connection with the Plateau Height, though less regularly. In the case of singly charged ions, such as in the first three salts listed in Table II, the PH is fairly close to that of water itself. It falls considerably where doubly charged ions, such as sulphate or calcium are present. And when the triply charged phosphate ion or ferric ion is present, the value sinks to merely a quarter of its value in water.

Time of Solution and Mixtures of Ions—Experiments currently in progress in these laboratories are concerned with the extremely important question of the variation of these endochronic properties of thiotimoline in the presence of mixtures of ions. The state of our data at present does not warrant very general conclusions, but even our preliminary work gives hope of the further development of the endochronic methods of analysis. Thus, in *Figure* 4, we have the endochronic curve where a mixture of 0·001 M Sodium Chloride and 0·001 Ferric Chloride solutions is the solvent. Here, two sharp changes in slope can be seen: the first at a solution time of −0·29, and the second at −1·13, these being the PH's characteristic of Ferric Chloride and Sodium Chloride respectively—see Table II. The PH for a given salt would thus appear not to be affected by the presence of other salts.

This is definitely not the case, however, for the PV, and it is to a quantitative elucidation of the variation of PV with impurities in the solvent that our major efforts are now directed.

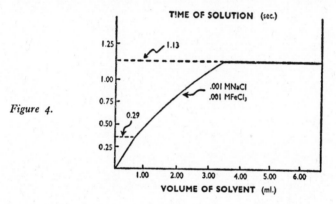

Figure 4.

Summary—Investigations of the endochronic qualities of thiotimoline have shown that:

a—Careful purification of the material is necessary for obtaining quantitative results.

b—Increasing the volume of solvent results in increasing the negative time of solution to a constant value known as the Plateau Height (PH), at a volume of solvent known as the Plateau Volume (PV).

c—The value of the PH is characteristic of the nature of the ions present in the solvent, varying with the ionic strength of the solution and not varying with the addition of other ions.

d—The value of the PV is characteristic of the concentration of the ions present in the solvent, being constant for different ions in solution of equal ionic strength, but varying markedly with the admixtures of second varieties of ions.

As a result of all this, it is suggested that endochronic methods offer a means of rapid—2 minutes or less—and accurate—within 0·1 per cent at least—analysis of inorganic, water-soluble materials.

REFERENCES

(1) P. Krum and L. Eshkin, *Journal of Chemical Solubilities*, *27*, 109–114 (1944), 'Concerning the Anomalous Solubility of Thiotimoline.'

(2) E. J. Feinschreiber and Y. Hravlek, *Journal of Chemical Solubilities*, *22*, 57–68 (1939), 'Solubility Speeds and Hydrophilic Groupings.'

(3) P. Krum, L. Eshkin, and O. Nile, *Annals of Synthetic Chemistry*, *115*, 1122–1145; 1208–1215 (1945), 'Structure of Thiotimoline, Parts I & II.'

(4) G. H. Freudler, *Journal of Psycho-chemistry*, *2*, 476–488 (1945), 'Initiative and Determination: Are They Influenced by Diet?—As tested by Thiotimoline solubility Experiments.'

(5) E. Harley-Short, *Philosophical Proceedings & Reviews*, *15*, 125–197 (1946). 'Determinism and Free-Will. The Application of Thiotimoline Solubility to Marxian Dialectic.'

(6) P. Krum, *Journal of Chemical Solubilities*, *29*, 818–719 (1946), 'A Device for the Quantitative Measurement of Thiotimoline Solubility Speed.'

(7) A. Roundin, B. Lev, and Y. J. Prutt, *Proceedings of the Society of Plant Chemistry*, *80*, 11–18 (1930), 'Natural Products isolated from shrubs of the genus *Rosacea*.'

PART II

Some years ago, the unusual endochronic properties of purified thiotimoline were first reported in this journal.[1] Despite the fascinating theoretical implications of these properties, thiotimoline research has languished, due largely to the distressing skepticism with which the first reports were met. This laboratory, however, due to the grants-in-aid made available to us by the American Association for the Advancement of Quantitative Psychiatry, has successfully extended its earlier observations in directions which were as unanticipated as they have proven fruitful.

It is the purpose of this present paper, in part, to show that by use of thiotimoline, certain mental disorders can be quantitated and their diagnosis converted from an uncertain art to an exact science.

The Endochronic Carbon Atom—As explained in detail in the previous paper on this subject, the unique property of thiotimoline is its extremely rapid rate of solution in distilled water. So rapid is this rate, indeed, that it dissolves 1·12 seconds *before* water is added. This endochronicity or 'negative solution time' is truly unique, as far as we know. Barosjek and Libnicz[2] report small endochronic effects in certain thiotimoline derivatives but we have been unable to confirm their findings.

Endochronicity is, of necessity, an inevitable consequence of the molecular structure of thiotimoline, and as a first assumption, one may lay the responsibility at the door of the versatile carbon atom. This is not the first time that an advance in our understanding of the carbon atom has led to a major advance in chemistry.

In the nineteenth century, it was pointed out that the four valence bonds of carbon were *not* distributed toward the points of a square (as, for convenience's sake, they still are on the blackboard and on the pages of textbooks) but toward the four vertices of a tetrahedron, (*see Figure* 5). The difference is that in the first case, all four bonds are distributed in a single plane,

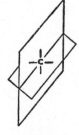

Figure 5. Planar and tetra-hedral carbon atoms. (N.B. In the tetrahedral atom the two light bonds may be pictured in the horizontal plane, and the two bold-face bonds in the vertical plane.)

a. Planar
Atom.

b. Tetrahedral
Atom.

while in the second, the bonds are divided, two and two, among two mutually perpendicular planes. The second view has made possible an explanation of phenomena such as optical isomerism which had been impossible to understand in the light of the older 'planar carbon atom'.

Now once more we can broaden our scope. We can pass from the 'tetrahedral carbon atom' to the 'endochronic carbon atom', in which the two planes of carbon valence bonds are not both spatial in the ordinary sense. One, instead, is temporal. It extends in time, that is. In the temporal plane, one bond extends toward yesterday and one toward tomorrow. Such a carbon atom cannot be presented on paper in the ordinary way and no effort will be made to do so.

Such an endochronic carbon atom is obviously very unstable and can occur only rarely, in fact only within the molecule of thiotimoline as far as we know. What there is in thiotimoline structure to cause this, what sort of super steric hindrance is as yet unknown, but the endochronic atom undoubtedly exists. As a result of its existence, a small portion of the thiotimoline molecule exists in the past and another small portion in the future.

It is this small portion of the molecule existing in the future which is dissolved by water which also exists in the future (*i.e.* is about to be added to the thiotimoline but has not yet been added). The remainder of the molecule is dragged into solution in the process and thus 'dissolves' in water which to all appear-ances is not there. Once this is understood, the mystery and apparent paradox disappears from thiotimoline's behaviour and the whole become something quite prosaic and amenable to mathematical analysis.

Such a mathematical analysis is now in preparation and will be submitted for publication at a future date. In connection with that, it may be stated briefly at the present time that the possession of endochronic properties necessitates the possession of exochronic properties as well. Considerable effort is being expended at our laboratories now to detect such exochronic properties. If, for instance, a small sample of thiotimoline solution at an original concentration of 1 milligram per milliliter is evaporated exceedingly quickly at temperatures low enough not to damage the molecule, it is obvious that thiotimoline ought to precipitate out of solution only 1·12 seconds *after* all the water has disappeared and not an instant before. Such phenomena have not yet been observed here, but we feel it to be only a question of developing appropriate techniques.

Endochronic Filtration—No factor has served to retard thiotimoline research as much as the difficulty of obtaining pure substance. Since relatively small traces of impurities mask the endochronic properties of thiotimoline and interfere with the reproducibility of quantitative measurements, considerable effort has perforce been expended on its thorough purification. Repeated recrystallization and resublimations have been necessary. The technique of endochronic filtration has been developed to simplify this procedure enormously.

As described in earlier papers, an extraction of the bark of the shrub, *Rosacea Karlsbadensis rufo* with distilled water at 5° C., followed by lyophilization (*i.e.* freeze-drying) of the extract, results in a faintly yellow powder one milligram of which will dissolve in 1 milliliter of water in −0·72 seconds. (It is important that this extraction not be extended for too long a period of time as the gradual extraction of the less soluble, non-endochronic components of the bark will rapidly destroy all traces of endochronicity in the final powder.)

Once an impure powder with significant endochronicity is obtained, only one further step is necessary to obtain extreme purity. The endochronic filter here shown (*see Figure* 6) is a simplified diagram taken from a detailed report from this

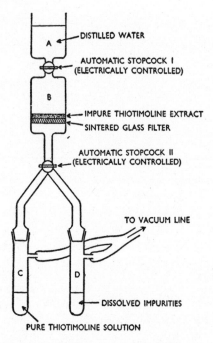

Figure 6. Simplified form of Endochronic filter.

laboratory on the principles of its mechanism.[3] It is only necessary here to describe the process briefly. The endochronic filter is essentially a device for rapid suction filtration. Stopcocks 1 and 2 are automatically controlled by an electric circuit not shown in this diagram. At the start of the process, stopcock 1 is in the closed position and 100 milliliters of distilled water are in vessel A. On the sintered glass filter of vessel B, not more than one gram of impure thiotimoline powdered extract is placed. Stopcock 2 (which is a two-way stopcock) is so turned as to connect vessels B and C. The electric circuit is then closed, an action which automatically turns on the vacuum pump. Five seconds after the electric circuit has been closed, a timer activates a relay which opens stopcock 1 and *simultaneously* turns stopcock 2 into its other position connecting vessels B and D.

The consequences of such a procedure are plain. At 0·72

seconds *before* stopcock 1 was opened, the thiotimoline molecules in the impure extract had dissolved in the water that was about to fall upon it while the non-thiotimoline molecules remained, of course impervious, to water whose existence was for them as yet only potential. Under the influence of the vacuum, the dissolved thiotimoline was sucked through the sintered glass filter and into vessel C. When stopcock 1 was opened, stopcock 2 was turned so as to allow any impurities that dissolved in the water which now *actually* fell upon the extract to be sucked into vessel D.

The solution in vessel C was lyophilized and one milligram of the white powder thus obtained was found to dissolve in one milliliter of water in $-1 \cdot 124$ seconds, a velocity somewhat more negative than had been attained by the use of the most highly purified samples of thiotimoline, as otherwise prepared. Trace ionic impurities present were derived, in all probability, from impurities in the distilled water used and did not interfere with the subsequent investigations.

The Endochronometroscope—The endochronometer, described in my previous communication to this journal, is essentially a device whereby a small cell containing powdered thiotimoline interrupts a light-beam which would otherwise be focused upon a photoelectric cell. Solution of the thiotimoline renders the cell transparent and the photoelectric cell is activated, closing the circuit and recording the exact time of solution. Since the water is added by an electrically-controlled automatic pipette, the time of addition of water can also be determined with great precision. The time of solution minus the time of addition is the 'endochronic interval'.

It has been increasingly apparent to workers in this laboratory that attention must be paid not only to the time at which thiotimoline dissolves but to its manner of dissolving. Lumbegger and Hophni of this laboratory have recently described a motion picture micro-camera (an 'endochronometroscope') attachment, by use of which fine deviations from the solubility norm can be detected.[4] Although the original purpose of this was to test certain theoretical implications of the endochronic carbon atom hypothesis, endochronometroscopy proved of the utmost importance in a series of experiments to be described below.

Willometry—It will be noted that the endochronic filter as well as the endochronometer are adjusted to work with a minimum of human interference. The necessity of this is obvious. Useless speculation has been brought forward in the past as to the possibility of withdrawing water *after* the thiotimoline has been dissolved and *before* the water has actually been added, thus 'fooling' the thiotimoline into dissolving in water which never arrives. In such a ridiculous attempt, needless to say, only the experimenters are fooled, since what they propose (if indeed they propose it seriously) runs counter to the second law of thermo-dynamics, as elementary calculation will show.[5]

Nevertheless, with ample supplies of thiotimoline of extreme purity finally made available by the use of endochronic filtration, it became possible to determine the effect of human will upon the negative time of solution (*i.e.* the endochronic interval) and, conversely, to measure the strength of the human will by means of thiotimoline. The resultant technique has been given the name, willometry.

It was early observed, for instance, that strong-willed, incisive personalities, achieved the full endochronic interval when adding water by hand. Having made up their minds, in other words, that they were going to add the water no doubts assailed them and the final addition was as certain as though it had been mechanically arranged.

Other individuals, of a more or less hesitating, self-deprecatory nature, yielded quite different results. Even when expressing themselves as entirely determined to add the water in response to a given signal, and though assuring us afterward that they had felt no hesitation, the time of negative solution decreased markedly. Undoubtedly, their inner hesitation was so deeply bound with their unconscious mind and with super-ego-censored infantile traumas that they were completely unaware of it in any conscious manner. The importance of such physical demonstrations, amenable to quantitative treatment, to the psychiatrist is obvious.

In a mass willometric experiment, 87 male students of the freshman class of Comstock Lode College (Crowded Creek, North Dakota) were used as subjects. It was found that the distribution of will-power varied in the ordinary bell-shaped probability curve. Two students yielded a time of solution of —1·10 seconds or better on all occasions and two students yielded an endochronic interval that was actually positive. It was interesting to note that among the female students (62 of whom were used in a similar experiment) the probability curve was somewhat skewed in the direction of stronger will (*see Figure* 7). Whereas the observed mean time of solution for all males subjects was —0·625, that for females was —0·811. This confirms a sex difference which has been intuitively apparent (to males, at least) through all of recorded time.

There is reason to think that the endochronic interval may vary with the immediate state of mind of a subject. One student, E. H., having yielded endochronic intervals of from —0·55 to —0·62 over a period of dozens of experiments, suddenly jumped the interval to —0·92. This increase in self-confidence appeared quite remarkable. The technician in charge of the experiment on close questioning insisted that no untoward event had taken place and, indeed, stated that the subject had done nothing more than to express the desire for a walk in the countryside that evening and that the technician had agreed to accompany him. Since E. H. was not particularly athletically inclined, it seemed strange that the prospects of a walk should so affect him. To test whether the effect could be rendered still

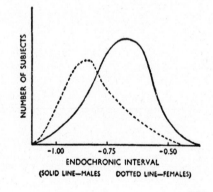

Figure 7. Distribution curve of endochronic intervals in males and females.

stronger, the author of this paper voluntarily offered to accompany E. H. as a third member of the party. Unaccountably, the endochronic interval dropped to −0·14 with the very next test. If we may be allowed some speculation, it may be that we are here in the presence of another sex difference made apparent by thiotimoline research, since the author of this paper is male (as was the student) while the technician is female—very pronouncedly female, in fact. Some facets of this obscure situation have been commented upon very recently by McLevinson.[6]

Schizophrenic Willometry—Lumbegger, of this laboratory, in the course of his endochronometroscopic observations on both mechanically and manually induced solutions of thiotimoline was the first to observe the anomalous behavior of thiotimoline under the influence of particular subjects.[7] Ordinarily, the thiotimoline powder dissolved with great rapidity (the time between completely solid state and completely dissolved state being less than a thousandth of a second) and with no perceptible unevenness. In the case of one subject, however, J. G. B., it was found that, strangely enough, there was a perceptible time during which part of the thiotimoline had dissolved and part had not. Dozens of repetitions of the experiments showed beyond all doubt that there was no flaw in the endochrononometer or endochronometroscope. A series of stills published in Lumbegger's paper, referred to above, make that quite clear.

The subject, however, when subjected to thoroughgoing psychoanalysis, promptly displayed hitherto undetected schizophrenic tendencies. The effect on the endochronic interval of two personalities of differing degrees of self-confidence within a single mind is obvious.

Through the kindness of Dr. Alan E. Windischgraets of the Psychosomatic Institute (Potlikker, Oklahoma) we were able to make use of 150 patients of varying schizophrenic tendencies as subjects for willometric studies.

These studies quickly indicated that three types of schizophrenic deviations from the normal may be detected endochronometroscopically. These may be termed *horizontal schizo-*

phrenia, vertical schizophrenia, and *diffuse schizophrenia.* In horizontal schizophrenia, the thiotimoline sample differs in its behavior about a horizontal line of cleavage. More commonly the upper half of the sample dissolves as much as 0·01 seconds before the lower half. This may be referred to as the *supra variety.* Less frequently it is the lower half that dissolves first and this is the *infra variety.*

Similarly, vertical schizophrenia evidences itself in variable solubility about a vertical line of cleavage. Here the left half of the sample dissolves first in about half the cases, and the right half in the other half. These are known respectively as the *levo variety* and the *dextro variety.* It has been a matter of some remark as to why the two varieties of vertical schizophrenia should be of equal occurrence while those of horizontal schizophrenia should be so unevenly represented in favor of the supra variety. There have been suggestions that the gravitational field plays its part in this, but no direct experimental evidence exists.

In diffuse schizophrenia, no neat dividing line exists between early-dissolving thiotimoline and late-dissolving thiotimoline. Rather the substance seems to dissolve in ragged patches randomly distributed through the body of the sample.

All these varieties of schizophrenia described above may be lumped together under the general name of *heteroschizophrenia,* since two personalities of different wills are involved. The heteroschizophrenics comprise by far the majority of the subjects tested. There remain, however, a few subjects who, from a psychiatric standpoint, show all the symptoms of schizophrenia, but who nevertheless show no discontinuities in the endochronic interval. The conclusion at which we have arrived is that these subjects possess two personalities of equal will and are, therefore, *isoschizophrenic.*

A summary of the distribution of patients in the various schizophrenic classes is given in Table III.

Each patient, in addition to being typed as one of the varieties listed above, can be further graded in accordance with the amount of deviation in the endochronic interval of the early-dissolving portions of thiotimoline and the late-dissolving portions. Since the maximum difference observed is about

TABLE III

*Distribution of Schizophrenic Classes among the Patients
at the Psychosomatic Institute*

Total Number of Patients Studied . .	150
Total Heteroschizophrenics	145
Vertical Schizophrenics	68
Levo Variety	33
Dextro Variety	35
Horizontal Schizophrenics	70
Supra Variety	62
Infra Variety	8
Diffuse Schizophrenics	7
Total Isoschizophrenics	5

0·010 seconds and since the endochronometroscope can easily detect time intervals of 0·001 seconds, ten grades may be distinguished, Grade 10 shows 0·010 seconds of deviations, Grade 9 shows 0·009 seconds of deviation and so on down to Grade 1 which shows 0·001 seconds of deviation.

In general, the lower grades are more frequently populated, as may be seen in Table IV. (It will be noted that only 145 patients are listed in Table IV. It is obvious that in the case of the 5 isoschizophrenics, Grade numbers are not applicable.)

TABLE IV

Grade Frequencies in all Varieties of Schizophrenia

Grade 1 . . 23	Grade 6 . . 8
Grade 2 . . 25	Grade 7 . . 6
Grade 3 . . 29	Grade 8 . . 9
Grade 4 . . 22	Grade 9 . . 5
Grade 5 . . 14	Grade 10 . . 4

Total Heteroschizophrenics . . 145

The value of such a subdivision of schizophrenia may well be said to be of incalculable potentialities and, indeed, to found a new science of *quantitative micropsychiatry*. How much more useful it is to say of a patient that he is a vertical schizophrenic, levo variety, Grade 3, than simply to say that he is schizophrenic.

If a small drawback exists in the magnificent structure now being erected, it is that all efforts have been so far unavailing in the attempt to find any medical meaning in our micropsychiatric divisions.[8] This failure of application should not however be allowed to diminish the aesthetic beauty and abstract symmetry of the new technique of endochronometroscopy and the science of quantitative micropsychiatry to which it has given birth.

REFERENCES

(1) I. Asimov, *The Endochronic Properties of Resublimated Thiotimoline*. Journal of Astounding Science Fiction, *50* (1), 120–125, (1948).

(2) H. A. Barosjek, and C. Z. Libnicz, *The Endochronic Properties. of Methylthiotimoline, Ethylthiotimoline and Isobutylthiotimoline* Acta Scandinavica Micropsychiatrica *1*, 273–281, (1950).

(3) T. Lumbegger, and A. E. Hophni, *A New Device for the Purification of Thiotimoline Based on the Principles of Endochronicity.* Analytical Psychochemistry *15*, 1–7, (1951).

(4) T. Lumbegger, and A. E. Hophni, *The Theoretical Basis of Endochronic Behavior as Indicated by Solution Phenomena.* Annals of Psychocolloid Behavior *123*, 403–406, (1951).

(5) O. W. Stannich, *The Paradoxes of Thiotimoline.* Zeitschrift für mathematischen Psychiatromessungen, *101*, 1129–1176, (1948).

(6) O. O. McLevinson, *Differences in Mental Attitude, as Measured by Thiotimoline Studies, of Walks with Members of One's Own and the Opposite Sex. New light on a puzzling problem.* Proceedings of the Society for the Entertainment of Servicemen *16*, 22–31, (1957).

(7) T. Lumbegger, *The Anomalous Behavior of Thiotimoline Under the Influence of a Particular Subject.* A preliminary note. Annals of Mental Biology, *66*, 123, (1950).

(8) A. E. Windischgraets, *Possible Correlations Between Patient Characteristics and the Micropsychiatric Values Revealed by Endochronometroscopic Measurements.* Proceedings of the Royal Society for Biophilosophical Research (London), Series B *128*, 92–109, (1952).

CHAPTER TWELVE

PATÉ DE FOIE GRAS

I COULDN'T tell you my real name if I wanted to and, under the circumstances, I don't want to.

I'm not much of a writer myself, unless you count the kind of stuff that passes muster in a scientific paper, so I'm having Isaac Asimov write this up for me.

I've picked him for several reasons. First, he's a biochemist, so he understands what I tell him; some of it, anyway. Secondly, he can write; or at least he has published considerable fiction, which may not, of course, be the same thing.

But most important of all, he can get what he writes published in science-fiction magazines and he has written two articles on thiotimoline, and that is exactly what I need for reasons that will become clear as we proceed.

I was not the first person to have the honor of meeting The Goose. That belongs to a Texas cotton farmer named Ian Angus MacGregor, who owned it before it became government property. (The names, places and dates I use are deliberately synthetic. None of you will be able to trace anything through them. Don't bother trying.)

MacGregor apparently kept geese about the place because they ate weeds, but not cotton. In this way, he had automatic weeders that were self-fueling and, in addition, produced eggs, down, and, at judicious intervals, roast goose.

By summer of 1955, he had sent an even dozen of letters to the Department of Agriculture requesting information on the hatching of goose-eggs. The Department sent him all the booklets on hand that were anywhere near the subject, but his letters simply got more impassioned and freer in their references to his 'friend', the local Congressman.

My connection with this is that I am in the employ of the Department of Agriculture. I have considerable training in agricultural chemistry, plus a smattering of vertebrate physiology. (This won't help you. If you think you can pin my identity out of this, you are mistaken.)

Since I was attending a convention at San Antonio in July of 1955, my boss asked me to stop off at MacGregor's place and see what I could do to help him. We're servants of the public and besides we had finally received a letter from MacGregor's congressman.

On July 17, 1955, I met The Goose.

I met MacGregor first. He was in his fifties, a tall man with a lined face full of suspicion. I went over all the information he had been given, explained about incubators, the values of trace minerals in the diet, plus some late information on Vitamin E, the cobalamins and the use of antibiotic additives.

He shook his head. He had tried it all and still the eggs wouldn't hatch. He had tried every gander he could get as co-workers in the deal and that hadn't helped either.

What could I do? I'm a Civil Service employee and not the archangel Gabriel. I'd told him all I could and if the eggs still wouldn't hatch, they wouldn't and that was that. I asked politely if I might see his geese, just so no one could say afterward I hadn't done all I possibly could.

He said, 'It's not geese, mister; it's one goose.'

I said, 'May I see the one goose?'

'Rather not.'

'Well, then, I can't help you any further. If it's only one goose, then there's just something wrong with it. Why worry about one goose? Eat it.'

I got up and reached for my hat.

He said, 'Wait!' and I stood there while his lips tightened and his eyes wrinkled and he had a quiet fight with himself.

He said, 'If I show you something, will you keep it secret?'

He didn't seem like the type of man to rely on another's vow of secrecy, but it was as though he had reached such a pit of desperation that he had no other way out.

I said, 'If it isn't anything criminal——'

'Nothing like that,' he snapped.

And then I went out with him to a pen near the house, surrounded by barbed wire, with a locked gate to it, and holding one goose—The Goose.

'That's The Goose,' he said. The way he said it, I could hear the capitals.

I stared at it. It looked like any other goose, heaven help me, fat, self-satisfied and short-tempered. I said, 'Hmm' in my best professional manner.

MacGregor said, 'And here's one of its eggs. It's been in the incubator. Nothing happens.' He produced it from a capacious overall pocket. There was a queer strain about his manner of holding it.

I frowned. There was something wrong with the egg. It was smaller and more spherical than normal.

MacGregor said, 'Take it.'

I reached out and took it. Or tried to. I gave it the amount of heft an egg like that ought to deserve and it just sat where it was. I had to try harder and then up it came.

Now I knew what was queer about the way MacGregor held it. It weighed nearly two pounds. (To be exact, when we weighed it later, we found its mass to be 852·6 grams.)

I stared at it as it lay there, pressing down the palm of my hand, and MacGregor grinned sourly. 'Drop it,' he said.

I just looked at him, so he took it out of my hand and dropped it himself.

It hit soggy. It didn't smash. There was no spray of white and yolk. It just lay where it fell with the bottom caved in.

I picked it up again. The white egg-shell had shattered where the egg had struck. Pieces of it had flaked away and what shone through was a dull yellow in color.

My hands trembled. It was all I could do to make my fingers work, but I got some of the rest of the shell flaked away, and stared at the yellow.

I didn't have to run any analyses. My heart told me.

I was face to face with The Goose!

The Goose That Laid The Golden Eggs!

You don't believe me. I'm sure of that. You've got this tabbed as another thiotimoline article.

Good! I'm *counting* on your thinking that. I'll explain later.

Meanwhile, my first problem was to get MacGregor to give up that golden egg. I was almost hysterical about it. I was almost ready to clobber him and make off with the egg by force if I had to.

I said, 'I'll give you a receipt. I'll guarantee you payment. I'll do anything in reason. Look, Mr. MacGregor, they're no good to you anyway. You can't cash the gold unless you can explain how it came into your possession. Holding gold is illegal. And how do you expect to explain? If the government——'

'I don't want the government butting in,' he said, stubbornly.

But I was twice as stubborn. I followed him about. I pleaded, I yelled. I threatened. It took me hours. Literally. In the end, I signed a receipt and he dogged me out to my car and stood in the road as I drove away, following me with his eyes.

He never saw that egg again. Of course, he was compensated for the value of the gold ($656.47 after taxes had been subtracted) but that was a bargain for the government.

When one considers the potential value of that egg——

The *potential* value! That's the irony of it. That's the reason for this article.

The head of my section at the Department of Agriculture is Louis P. Bronstein. (Don't bother looking him up. The 'P.' stands for Pittfield if you want more misdirection.)

He and I are on good terms and I felt I could explain things without being placed under immediate observation. Even so, I took no chances. I had the egg with me and when I got to the tricky part, I just laid it on the desk between us.

Finally, he touched it with his finger as though it were hot.

I said, 'Pick it up.'

It took him a long time, but he did, and I watched him take two tries at it as I had.

I said, 'It's a yellow metal and it could be brass only it isn't because it's inert to concentrated nitric acid. I've tried that already. There's only a shell of gold because it can be bent with moderate pressure. Besides, if it were solid gold, the egg would weigh over ten pounds.'

Bronstein said, 'It's some sort of hoax. It *must* be.'

'A hoax that uses real gold? Remember, when I first saw this thing, it was covered completely with authentic unbroken egg-shell. It's been easy to check a piece of the egg-shell. Calcium carbonate. That's a hard thing to gimmick. And if we look inside the egg (I didn't want to do that on my own, chief) and find real egg, then we've got it, because that would be impossible to gimmick. Surely, this is worth an official project.'

'How can I approach the Secretary with——' He stared at the egg.

But he did in the end. He made phone calls and sweated out most of a day. One or two of the Department brass came to look at the egg.

Project Goose was started. That was July 20, 1955.

I was the responsible investigator to begin with and remained in titular charge throughout, though matters quickly got beyond me.

We began with the one egg. It's average radius was 35 millimeters (major axis, 72 millimeters; minor axis, 68 millimeters). The gold shell was 2·45 millimeters in thickness. Studying other eggs later on, we found this value to be rather high. The average thickness turned out to be 2·1 millimeters.

Inside *was* egg. It looked like egg and it smelled like egg.

Aliquots were analyzed and the organic constituents were reasonably normal. The white was 9·7 per cent albumin. The yolk had the normal complement of vitellin, cholesterol, phospholipid and carotenoid. We lacked enough material to test for trace constituents but later on with more eggs at our disposal we did and nothing unusual showed up as far as the contents of vitamins, coenzymes, nucleotides, sulfhydryl groups, etc., etc., were concerned.

One important gross abnormality that showed was the eggs behavior on heating. A small portion of the yolk, heated, 'hardboiled' almost at once. We fed a portion of the hard-boiled egg to a mouse. It survived.

I nibbled at another bit of it. Too small a quantity to taste, really, but it made me sick. Purely psychosomatic, I'm sure.

Boris W. Finley, of the Department of Biochemistry of Temple University (a Department consultant) supervised these tests.

He said, referring to the hard-boiling, "The ease with which the egg-proteins are heat-denatured indicates a partial denaturation to begin with and, considering the nature of the shell, the obvious guilt would lie at the door of heavy-metal contamination.'

So a portion of the yolk was analyzed for inorganic constituents, and it was found to be high in chloraurate ion, which is a singly-charged ion containing an atom of gold and four of chlorine, the symbol for which is $AuCl_4^-$. (The 'Au' symbol for gold comes from the fact that the Latin word for gold is 'aurum'). When I say the chloraurate ion content was high, I mean it was 3·2 parts per thousand, or 0·32 per cent. That's high enough to form insoluble complexes of 'gold-protein' which would coagulate easily.

Finley said, 'It's obvious this egg cannot hatch. Nor can any other such egg. It is heavy-metal poisoned. Gold may be more glamorous than lead but it is just as poisonous to proteins.'

I agreed gloomily, 'At least it's safe from decay, too.'

'Quite right. No self-respecting bug would live in this chlorauriferous soup.'

The final spectrographic analysis of the gold of the shell came in. Virtually pure. The only detectable impurity was iron which amounted to 0·23 per cent of the whole. The iron content of the egg yolk had been twice normal, also. At the moment, however, the matter of the iron was neglected.

One week after Project Goose was begun, an expedition was sent into Texas. Five biochemists went (the accent was still on biochemistry, you see) along with three truckloads of equipment, and a squadron of army personnel. I went along, too, of course.

As soon as we arrived, we cut MacGregor's farm off from the world.

That was a lucky thing, you know—the security measures we took right from the start. The reasoning was wrong, at first, but the results were good.

The Department wanted Project Goose kept quiet at the start simply because there was always the thought that this might still be an elaborate hoax and we couldn't risk the bad publicity, if it were. And if it weren't a hoax, we couldn't risk the newspaper hounding that would definitely result for any goose-and-golden-egg story.

It was only well after the start of Project Goose, well after our arrival at MacGregor's farm, that the real implications of the matter became clear.

Naturally, MacGregor didn't like the men and equipment settling down all about him. He didn't like being told The Goose was government property. He didn't like having his eggs impounded.

He didn't like it but he agreed to it—if you can call it agreeing when negotiations are being carried on while a machine gun is being assembled in a man's barnyard and ten men, with bayonets fixed, are marching past while the arguing is going on.

He was compensated, of course. What's money to the government?

The Goose didn't like a few things, either—like having blood samples taken. We didn't dare anesthetize it for fear of doing anything to alter its metabolism, and it took two men to hold it each time. Ever try to hold an angry goose?

The Goose was put under a twenty-four hour guard with the threat of summary court-martial to any man who let anything happen to it. If any of those soldiers read this article, they may get a sudden glimmering of what was going on. If so, they will probably have the sense to keep shut about it. At least, if they know what's good for them, they will.

The blood of The Goose was put through every test conceivable.

It carried 2 parts per hundred thousand (0·002 per cent) of chloraurate ion. Blood taken from the hepatic vein was richer than the rest, almost 4 parts per hundred thousand.

Finley grunted. 'The liver,' he said.

We took X-rays. On the X-ray negative, the liver was a cloudy mass of light gray, lighter than the viscera in its neighborhood, because it stopped more of the X-rays, because it contained more gold. The blood vessels showed up lighter than the liver proper and the ovaries were pure white. No X-rays got through the ovaries at all.

It made sense and in an early report, Finley stated it as bluntly as possible. Paraphrasing the report, it went, in part:

'The chloraurate ion is secreted by the liver into the blood stream. The ovaries act as a trap for the ion, which is there reduced to metallic gold and deposited as a shell about the developing egg. Relatively high concentrations of unreduced chloraurate ion penetrate the contents of the developing egg.

'There is little doubt that The Goose finds this process useful as a means of getting rid of the gold atoms which, if allowed to accumulate, would undoubtedly poison it. Excretion by egg-shell may be novel in the animal kingdom, even unique, but there is no denying that it is keeping The Goose alive.

'Unfortunately, however, the ovary is being locally poisoned to such an extent that few eggs are laid, probably not more than will suffice to get rid of the accumulating gold, and those few eggs are definitely unhatchable.'

That was all he said in writing, but to the rest of us, he said, 'That leaves one peculiarly embarrassing question.'

I knew what it was. We all did.

Where was the gold coming from?

No answer to that for a while, except for some negative evidence. There was no perceptible gold in The Goose's feed, nor were there any gold-bearing pebbles about that it might have swallowed. There was no trace of gold anywhere in the soil of the area and a search of the house and grounds revealed nothing. There were no gold coins, gold jewelry, gold plate, gold watches, or gold anything. No one on the farm even had as much as gold fillings in his teeth.

There was Mrs. MacGregor's wedding ring, of course, but she had only had one in her life and she was wearing that one.

So where was the gold coming from?

The beginnings of the answer came on August 16, 1955.

Albert Nevis, of Purdue, was forcing gastric tubes into The Goose (another procedure to which the bird objected strenu-ously) with the idea of testing the contents of its alimentary canal. It was one of our routine searches for exogenous gold.

Gold *was* found, but only in traces and there was every reason to suppose those traces had accompanied the digestive secretions and were therefore endogenous (from within, that is) in origin.

However, something else showed up, or the lack of it, anyway.

I was there when Nevis came into Finley's office in the temporary building we had put up overnight (almost) near the goosepen.

Nevis said, 'The Goose is low in bile pigment. Duodenal contents show about none.'

Finley frowned and said, 'Liver function is probably knocked loop-the-loop because of its gold concentration. It probably isn't secreting bile at all.'

'It *is* secreting bile,' said Nevis. 'Bile acids are present in normal quantity. Near normal, anyway. It's just the bile pigments that are missing. I did a fecal analysis and that was confirmed. No bile pigments.'

Let me explain something at this point. Bile acids are steroids secreted by the liver into the bile and *via* that are poured into the upper end of the small intestine. These bile acids are detergent-like molecules which help to emulsify the fat in our diet (or The Goose's) and distribute them in the form of tiny bubbles through the watery intestinal contents. This distribution, or homogenization, if you'd rather, makes it easier for the fat to be digested.

Bile pigments, the substance that was missing in The Goose, are something entirely different. The liver makes them out of hemoglobin, the red oxygen-carrying protein of the blood. Wornout hemoglobin is broken up in the liver, the heme part being split away. The heme is made up of a ring-like molecule (called a 'porphyrin') with an iron atom in the center. The liver takes the iron out and stores it for future use, then breaks the ring-like molecule that is left. This broken porphyrin is bile pigment. It is colored brownish or greenish (depending on further chemical changes) and is secreted into the bile.

The bile pigments are of no use to the body. They are poured into the bile as waste products. They pass through the intestines and come out with the feces. In fact, the bile pigments are responsible for the color of the feces.

Finley's eyes began to glitter.

Nevis said, 'It looks as though porphyrin catabolism isn't following the proper course in the liver. Doesn't it to you?'

It surely did. To me, too.

There was tremendous excitement after that. This was the first metabolic abnormality, not directly involving gold, that had been found in The Goose!

We took a liver biopsy (which means we punched a cylindrical sliver out of The Goose reaching down into the liver). It hurt The Goose but didn't harm it. We took more blood samples, too.

This time, we isolated hemoglobin from the blood and small quantities of the cytochromes from our liver samples. (The cytochromes are oxidizing enzymes that also contain heme.) We separated out the heme and in acid solution some of it precipitated in the form of a brilliant orange substance. By August 22, 1955, we had 5 micrograms of the compound.

The orange compound was similar to heme, but it was not heme. The iron in heme can be in the form of a doubly charged ferrous ion (Fe^{++}) or a triply charged ferric ion (Fe^{+++}), in which latter case, the compound is called hematin. (Ferrous and ferric, by the way, come from the Latin word for iron, which is 'ferrum'.)

The orange compound we had separated from heme had the porphyrin portion of the molecule all right, but the metal in the center was gold, to be specific, a triply charged auric ion (Au^{+++}). We called this compound 'aureme', which is simply short for 'auric heme'.

Aureme was the first naturally-occurring gold-containing organic compound ever discovered. Ordinarily, it would rate headline news in the world of biochemistry. But now it was nothing; nothing at all in comparison to the further horizons its mere existence opened up.

The liver, it seemed, was not breaking up the heme to bile pigment. Instead it was converting it to aureme; it was replacing iron with gold. The aureme, in equilibrium with chloraurate ion, entered the blood stream and was carried to the ovaries where the gold was separated out and the porphyrin portion of the molecule disposed of by some as yet unidentified mechanism.

Further analyses showed that 29 per cent of the gold in the blood of The Goose was carried in the plasma in the form of chloraurate ion. The remaining 71 per cent was carried in the red blood corpuscles in the form of 'auremoglobin'. An attempt was made to feed The Goose traces of radioactive gold so that we could pick up radioactivity in plasma and corpuscles and see how readily the auremoglobin molecules were handled in the ovaries. It seemed to us the auremoglobin should be much more slowly disposed of than the dissolved chloraurate ion in the plasma.

The experiment failed, however, since we detected no radio-activity. We put it down to inexperience since none of us were isotopes men and that was too bad since the failure was highly significant, really, and by not realizing it, we lost several days.

The auremoglobin was, of course, useless as far as carrying oxygen was concerned, but it only made up about 0·1 per cent of the total hemoglobin of the red blood cells so there was no interference with the respiration of The Goose.

This still left us with the question of where the gold came from and it was Nevis who first made the crucial suggestion.

'Maybe,' he said, at a meeting of the group held on the evening of August 25, 1955, 'Maybe The Goose doesn't replace the iron with gold. Maybe it *changes* the iron to gold.'

Before I met Nevis personally that summer, I had known him through his publications (his field is bile chemistry and liver function) and had always considered him a cautious, clear-thinking person. Almost over-cautious. One wouldn't consider him capable for a minute of making any such completely ridiculous statement.

It just shows the desperation and demoralization involved in Project Goose.

The desperation was the fact that there was nowhere, literally nowhere, that the gold could come from. The Goose was excreting gold at the rate of 38·9 grams of gold a day and had been doing it over a period of months. That gold had to come from somewhere and, failing that—absolutely failing that—it had to be made from something.

The demoralization that led us to consider the second alternative was due to the mere fact that we were face to face with The Goose That Laid The Golden Eggs; the undeniable GOOSE. With that, everything became possible. All of us were living in a fairy-tale world and all of us reacted to it by losing all sense of reality.

Finley considered the possibility seriously. 'Hemoglobin,' he said, 'enters the liver and a bit of auremoglobin comes out. The gold shell of the eggs has iron as its only impurity. The egg yolk is high in only two things; in gold, of course, and also, somewhat, in iron. It all makes a horrible kind of distorted sense. We're going to need help, men.'

We did and it meant a third stage of the investigation. The first stage had consisted of myself alone. The second was the biochemical task-force. The third, the greatest, the most important of all, involved the invasion of the nuclear physicists.

On September 5, 1955, John L. Billings of the University of California arrived. He had some equipment with him and more arrived in the following weeks. More temporary structures were going up. I could see that within a year we would have a whole research institution built about The Goose.

Billings joined our conference the evening of the 5th.

Finley brought him up to date, and said, 'There are a great many serious problems involved in this iron-to-gold idea. For one thing, the total quantity of iron in The Goose can only be of the order of half a gram, yet nearly 40 grams of gold a day are being manufactured.'

Billings had a clear, high-pitched voice. He said, 'There's a worse problem than that. Iron is about at the bottom of the packing fraction curve. Gold is much higher up. To convert a gram of iron to a gram of gold takes just about as much energy as is produced by the fissioning of one gram of U-235.'

Finley shrugged. 'I'll leave the problem to you.'

Billings said, 'Let me think about it.'

He did more than think. One of the things done was to isolate fresh samples of heme from The Goose, ash it and send the iron oxide to Brookhaven for isotopic analysis. There was no particular reason to do that particular thing. It was just one of a number of individual investigations, but it was the one that brought results.

When the figures came back, Billings choked on them. He said, 'There's no Fe^{56}.'

'What about the other isotopes?' asked Finley at once.

'All present,' said Billings, 'in the appropriate relative ratios, but no detectable Fe^{56}.'

I'll have to explain again. Iron, as it occurs naturally, is made up of four different isotopes. These isotopes are varieties of atoms that differ from one another in atomic weight. Iron atoms with an atomic weight of 56, or Fe^{56}, makes up 91·6 per cent of all the atoms in iron. The other atoms have atomic weights of 54, 57 and 58.

The iron from the heme of The Goose was made up only of Fe^{54}, Fe^{57} and Fe^{58}. The implication was obvious. Fe^{56} was disappearing while the other isotopes weren't and this meant a nuclear reaction was taking place. A nuclear reaction could take one isotope and leave others be. An ordinary chemical reaction, any chemical reaction at all, would have to dispose of all isotopes equally.

'But it's energically impossible,' said Finley.

He was only saying that in mild sarcasm with Billings' initial remark in mind. As biochemists, we knew well enough that many reactions went on in the body which required an input of energy and that this was taken care of by coupling the energy-demanding reaction with an energy-producing reaction.

However, chemical reactions gave off or took up a few kilocalories per mole. Nuclear reactions gave off or took up millions. To supply energy for an energy-demanding nuclear reaction required, therefore a second, and energy-producing nuclear reaction.

We didn't see Billings for two days.

When he did come back, it was to say, 'See here, The energy-producing reaction must produce just as much energy per nucleon involved as the energy-demanding reaction uses up. If it produces even slightly less, then the over-all reaction won't go. If it produces even slightly more, then considering the astronomical number of nucleons involved, the excess energy produced would vaporize The Goose in a fraction of a second.'

'So?' said Finley.

'So the number of reactions possible is very limited. I have been able to find only one plausible system. Oxygen–18, if converted to iron–56 will produce enough energy to drive the iron–56 on to gold–197. It's like going down one side of a roller-coaster and then up the other. We'll have to test this.'

'How?'

'First, suppose we check the isotopic composition of the oxygen in The Goose.'

Oxygen is made up of three stable isotopes, almost all of it O^{16}. O^{18} makes up only one oxygen atom out of 250.

Another blood sample. The water content was distilled off in vacuum and some of it put through a mass spectrograph. There was O^{18} there but only one oxygen atom out of 1300. Fully 80 per cent of the O^{18} we expected wasn't there.

Billings said, 'That's corroborative evidence. Oxygen–18 is being used up. It is being supplied constantly in the food and water fed to The Goose, but it is still being used up. Gold–197 is being produced. Iron–56 is one intermediate and since the reaction that uses up iron–56 is faster than the one that produces it, it has no chance to reach significant concentration and isotopic analysis shows its absence.

We weren't satisfied, so we tried again. We kept The Goose for a week on water that had been enriched with O^{18}. Gold production went up almost at once. At the end of a week, it was producing 45·8 grams while the O^{18} content of its body water was no higher than before.

'There's no doubt about it,' said Billings.

He snapped his pencil and stood up. 'That Goose is a living nuclear reactor.'

The Goose was obviously a mutation.

A mutation suggested radiation among other things and radiation brought up the thought of nuclear tests conducted in 1952 and 1953 several hundred miles away from the site of MacGregor's farm. (If it occurs to you that no nuclear tests have been conducted in Texas, it just shows two things; I'm not telling you everything and you don't know everything.)

I doubt that at any time in the history of the atomic era was background radiation so thoroughly analyzed and the radioactive content of the soil so rigidly sifted.

Back records were studied. It didn't matter how top-secret they were. By this time, Project Goose had the highest priority that had ever existed.

Even weather records were checked in order to follow the behavior of the winds at the time of the nuclear tests.

Two things turned up.

One: The background radiation at the farm was a bit higher than normal. Nothing that could possibly do harm, I hasten to add. There were indications, however, that at the time of the birth of The Goose, the farm had been subjected to the drifting edge of at least two fallouts. Nothing really harmful, I again hasten to add.

Second: The Goose, alone of all geese on the farm; in fact, alone of all living creatures on the farm that could be tested, including the humans, showed no radioactivity at all. Look at it this way: *everything* shows traces of radioactivity; that's what is meant by background radiation. But The Goose showed none.

Finley sent one report on December 6, 1955, which I can paraphrase as follows:

'The Goose is a most extraordinary mutation, born of a high-level radioactivity environment which at once encouraged mutations in general and which made this particular mutation a beneficial one.

'The Goose has enzyme systems capable of catalyzing various nuclear reactions. Whether the enzyme system consists of one enzyme or more than one is not known. Nor is anything known of the nature of the enzymes in question. Nor can any theory be yet advanced as to how an enzyme can catalyze a nuclear reaction, since these involve particulate interactions with forces five orders of magnitude higher than those involved in the ordinary chemical reactions commonly catalyzed by enzymes.

'The overall nuclear change is from oxygen–18 to gold–197. The oxygen–18 is plentiful in its environment, being present in significant amount in water and all organic foodstuffs. The gold–197 is excreted via the ovaries. One known intermediate is iron–56 and the fact that auremogiobin is formed in the process leads us to suspect that the enzyme or enzymes involved may have heme as a prosthetic group.

'There has been considerable thought devoted to the value this overall nuclear change might have to the goose. The oxygen–18 does it no harm and the gold–197 is troublesome to be rid of, potentially poisonous, and a cause of its sterility. Its formation might possibly be a means of avoiding greater danger. This danger——'

But just reading it in the report, friend, makes it all seem so quiet, almost pensive. Actually, I never saw a man come closer to apoplexy and survive than Billings did when he found out about our own radioactive gold experiments which I told you about earlier—the ones in which we detected no radioactivity in the goose, so that we discarded the results as meaningless.

Many times over he asked how we could possibly consider it unimportant that we had lost radioactivity.

'You're like the cub reporter,' he said, 'who was sent to cover a society wedding and returning saying there was no story because the groom hadn't shown up.

'You fed The Goose radioactive gold and lost it. Not only that you failed to detect any natural radioactivity about The Goose. Any carbon–14. Any potassium–40. And you called it failure.'

We started feeding The Goose radioactive isotopes. Cautiously, at first, but before the end of January of 1956 we were shovelling it in.

The Goose remained non-radioactive.

'What it amounts to,' said Billings, 'is that this enzyme-catalyzed nuclear process of The Goose manages to convert any unstable isotope into a stable isotope.'

'Useful,' I said.

'Useful? It's a thing of beauty. It's the perfect defense against the atomic age. Listen, the conversion of oxygen–18 to gold–197 should liberate eight and a fraction positrons per oxygen atom. That means eight and a fraction gamma rays as soon as each positron combines with an electron. No gamma-rays either. The Goose must be able to absorb gamma rays harmlessly.'

We irradiated The Goose with gamma-rays. As the level rose, The Goose developed a slight fever and we quit in panic. It was just fever, though, not radiation sickness. A day passed, the fever subsided, and The Goose was as good as new.

'Do you see what we've got?' demanded Billings.

'A scientific marvel,' said Finley.

'Good Lord, don't you see the practical applications. If we could find out the mechanism and duplicate it in the test-tube, we've got a perfect method of radioactive ash disposal. The most important gimmick preventing us from going ahead with a full-scale atomic economy is the thought of what to do with the radioactive isotopes manufactured in the process. Sift them through an enzyme preparation in large vats and that would be it.

'Find out the mechanism, gentlemen, and you can stop worrying about fallouts. We would find a protection against radiation sickness.

'Alter the mechanism somehow and we can have Geese excreting any element needed. How about uranium–235 eggshells.

'The mechanism! The mechanism!'

He could shout 'Mechanism' all he wanted. It did no good.

We sat there, all of us, staring at The Goose and sitting on our hands.

If only the eggs would hatch. If only we could get a tribe of nuclear-reactor Geese.

'It must have happened before,' said Finley. 'The legends of such Geese must have started somehow.'

'Do you want to wait?' asked Billings.

If we had a gaggle of such Geese, we could begin taking a few apart. We could study its ovaries. We could prepare tissue slices and tissue homogenates.

That might not do any good. The tissue of a liver biopsy did not react with oxygen–18 under any conditions we tried.

But then we might perfuse an intact liver. We might study intact embryos, watch for one to develop the mechanism.

But with only one Goose, we could do none of that.

We don't dare kill The Goose That Lays The Golden Eggs.

The secret was in the liver of that fat Goose.

Liver of fat goose! *Paté de foie gras!* No delicacy to us!

Nevis said, thoughtfully, 'We need an idea. Some radical departure. Some crucial thought.'

'Saying it won't bring it,' said Billings despondently.

And in a miserable attempt at a joke, I said, 'We could advertise in the newspapers,' and that gave *me* an idea.

'Science-fiction!' I said.

'What?' said Finley.

'Look, science-fiction magazines print gag articles. The readers consider it fun. They're interested.' I told them about the thiotimoline articles Asimov wrote and which I had once read.

The atmosphere was cold with disapproval.

'We won't even be breaking security regulations,' I said, 'because no one will believe it.' I told them about the time in 1944 when Cleve Cartmill wrote a story describing the atom bomb one year early and the F.B.I. kept its temper.

They just stared at me.

'And science-fiction readers have ideas. Don't underrate them. Even if they think it's a gag article, they'll send their notions in to the editor. And since we have no ideas of our own; since we're up a dead-end street, what can we lose?'

They still didn't buy it.

So I said, 'And you know—The Goose won't live forever.'

That did it, somehow.

We had to convince Washington; then I got in touch with John Campbell, the science-fiction editor, and he got in touch with Asimov.

Now the article is done. I've read it, I approve, and I urge you all not to believe it. Please don't.

Only——

Any ideas?